Ticket To Sugarloaf

Hope you enjoy this,
Jill.

Jill Madden

CALDER WOOD PRESS

2013

Ticket to Sugarloaf, By Jill Madden

Published by **Calder Wood Press**
1 Beachmont Court, Dunbar, EH42 1YF
www.calderwoodpress.co.uk

ISBN: 978-1-902629-48-3

Jill Madden was born in Crewe, Cheshire, in 1940 and moved to Scotland in 2007. She now lives in Dunbar. She worked as an English and Drama teacher and later as a Psychotherapist and Counsellor.

About her collection of stories, Jill says, "Some of them are true and some of them are not. They capture memories both real and imaginary."

Printed by **MDPD**, 20 Fisherrow Industrial Estate, Newhailes Road, Musselburgh EH21 6RU Tel: 0131 653 2641

Preface

Collecting my stories together in a book was an idea I carried in my head, unsure if it would ever happen. Thank you, Johnny, for inspiring me on that Christmas visit in 2011. Your words made me want to turn the idea into reality.

Many thanks to all those who have supported and encouraged me throughout the creation of this book:

Big thanks to Jo Gibson for all her help, advice, and resolve in putting this together. Thanks to Elspeth Brown for proofreading, Sarah Madden for helping, and Karen Dietz for word processing. Thanks to Gordon Jenkinson for his photographs, artwork, and generous amounts of time given so freely. Thank you to the Dunbar Writers for believing in my writing, and for their friendship.

Diana Hendry - poet, writer, and broadcaster – judged the Tyne & Esk Writer of the Year competition in 2008, and chose my entry, *Ticket To Sugarloaf*, as the winning story; thank you.

For Sarah and Johnny

CONTENTS

Headlines

When he looked directly at you with his vivid blue eyes and smiled his wide smile, you glimpsed an unexpected inner world, a world all his own, and you wanted to travel there with him.

He worked on the railways as a platelayer. Every day he joined a gang of men responsible for maintaining the railway lines. He liked the job. It led him away from the shunting yards and the coal dust where the giant steam engines pushed and pulled their wagons. As he left the sidings, the clanking and clashing faded and then he was free. His workmates would call out instructions but he knew his job well. He was not an ambitious man, and the straight metal lines comforted him.

Joseph Madden had one great love in his life. Born and brought up in southern Ireland, he had spent his childhood with horses. He rode through his dreams of becoming a jockey, and he knew he would never be wealthy enough to own horses, but he needed to remain connected with them.

Near to his terraced house, where he lived with his wife Martha and their large family of born-close-together children, there was a large cattle market. It became his bolthole. Every Sunday he would work with the Shire horses, plaiting their manes and tails around brightly coloured ribbons and combing out the 'feathers' around their huge hooves. He was given the job of showing them off in the cattle ring, leading them round and round on decorated ropes.

Some were difficult and dangerous and he would be sent for. He calmed them. He would breathe gently into their wide whiskery nostrils, pull firmly on their thick leathery lower lips and rub their yellowing teeth and gums. Then he would talk to them. Nobody could hear his words, but the horses would relax and let him step underneath them from side to side, and, like giant pillows, they would let him lean against them.

Occasionally, as he worked clearing the long grass from around the railway lines, there would be a sharp warning call and he would stand back to let a huge steam engine thunder past. The size and the power and the grandeur of these engines reminded him of the Shire horses.

His love of horses extended to gambling. Any spare money was spent in the betting shop, more so once his children were grown and had left home.

His sons had spread out in all directions: his eldest son to the army, the next to work on the railways, and the youngest to teach at the local technical college. The three girls were expected to marry, but only one did. Another daughter, restless and troubled, kept running away from home, and finally was committed to a mental hospital; she never came back. Her mother banned her name and any mention or memory of her; it was as if she had never existed.

The house became a gloomy place and the feeling of uncertainty in the house deepened; soon afterwards, the eldest daughter left home for New Zealand in search of a new life. The atmosphere in the deserted home darkened. Conversation dried up and illness crept through the damp brickwork and lodged like a cancer.

He still went to work. Night duty was better paid and he liked it. The money reassured his wife, and the night reassured him.

There was talk of war; the engines pulled their deadly loads of bombs through the secret darkness. Men in uniform waved from the dimly lit carriages, and he would wave back. He wondered if they were saying hello to him, or goodbye to England.

Wildlife thrived along the edges of the railway lines in the thick grasses. Wildflowers, mice, shrews, glow-worms, toads, grass snakes, hedgehogs, all lived undisturbed. He watched stoats hunting, and owls, like giant moths, flew into the smoke, giddied by the heat and light. Mostly, the shock killed them, and one night he collected a big bagful of the large sad creatures. They were so beautiful, even in death. He took them home and put one in every empty flower vase, so that his wife could share them. Her screams woke him and he found her crumpled on the floor. "You know I'm dying and yet you surround me with death," she sobbed. "You stupid, useless man."

He hadn't known. He gathered up the owls silently and left the room.

Death visited every day now. It was tangible. He could almost taste it. The trains carried it through the night and his wife grew weaker every day.

He was more useful away from home, and as he worked he thought about his own life. It was like getting to know a stranger. He missed his daughters. Most of all he missed the one who had left the country, barely out of her teens. She was pretty, bright, and adventurous. She wrote home often; long, interesting, lively letters. More letters arrived when she travelled to Canada, and then exactly one year after leaving she arrived home on a visit.

With her arrival the gloom lifted from the house. It was as if spring had arrived in January. He looked forward to coming home. She visited her old school friends and talked so vividly about the people she'd met and worked for, he felt he knew them too.

She moved quickly, like a bird, taking everything in; chattering, laughing, exploring, and then – just like a bird – she left and returned to New Zealand, where she had no family or friends.

As the night shift wore on he continued to think, revisiting his middle daughter. He tried to imagine her life now, locked up in an institution only a bus ride away. The thought of this terrified him, and yet some memories made him smile; of her, as a young girl, standing defiant at the back of the local church, shouting at the vicar. "This is all rubbish; all this talk of God and punishment and Hell. You and my mother have got it all wrong. The policeman should come and take you away, bloody well take you away."

The policeman did come in the end, and the doctor, but they took his daughter away and he never saw her again.

Unlike his daughter who had travelled thousands of miles away but was wrapped around his heart always, his youngest daughter, flighty, girly, and nosy, had never crept into his heart. She was a kind little thing with curly brown hair, round brown eyes, long stick legs, and narrow flat feet, so big that she often cut the toe ends off her shoes so that they would fit her. She didn't care what people thought of her. She had giggled her way into marriage with a docile man who adored her, and she travelled twenty yards to live all her life across the road from her parents, where she haphazardly helped her docile husband to look after her mother.

He shuddered towards February. Nothing warmed him and an ominous feeling settled over him like a mist. He spoke less to his work mates now, and only nodded goodbye as he trudged up the steps to the station top.

A small group of people were gathered around a newspaper billboard. Oddly, they stopped talking as he approached. He read the headline:

CREWE GIRL MURDERED
VICTIM IDENTIFIED
TAHEKE, NEW ZEALAND

Metamorphosis

I remember my first chrysalis – a veined, leafy thing crisply wedged
in a splintered log. I kneeled down and prodded it. It twitched.
When I gently held its tiny waist and squeezed, it danced its lower
half from side to side, dead but still alive. I was fascinated. Who was
in there, and why?
I visited it every day and squeezed its waist.
One day it didn't dance, so I squeezed it harder.
It burst its slimy yellow insides all over my fingers.
It felt worse than a death.

Ring On a Ribbon

My father had decided never to have a child. It was a clear-cut decision formed in a web of silent, secret thoughts wreathed round with mystery and unspoken fears, still lingering in me.

My mother was a pretty, smiling woman; eternally innocent, constantly loving, pliable and pleasing. They raced through the working-class railway town of Crewe on an Ariel motorbike, dressed in their stylish leathers, free as birds and vastly envied. People muttered their disapproval. "Those two deserve twins," said one woman.

They were filled with their dreams. My father rented a farm cottage and continued working on the railway. My mother arranged and sold flowers in a local florist's shop, working long hours and earning little.

And then, just as in the storybooks, he whisked her away on the back of his motorbike to the nearby village of Nantwich and married her in the registry office, choosing two cleaners to witness the event. The deed was done, but, terrified by a fiercely possessive and domineering mother, she threaded her wedding ring onto a ribbon, and, tying it around her neck, returned to live with her family. She was 28 years of age and had courted my Father for twelve years.

My father moved into the cottage, bought a red Morgan sports car, and enraged my grandmother each time he roared up the street to capture my mother and drive her away from her family.

A year passed, and the wedding ring hung like a secret round my mother's neck until, one day, my suspicious grandmother, in her daily search through my mother's room, found her treasure box unlocked. There lay the marriage certificate, carefully folded and hidden under some dried flowers, dusty with memories. Within two days, my mother was installed in the cottage, the flower arranging replaced by a job at a local sewing factory, and a second-hand pushbike was bought and propped up against the wall.

Their two dreams crashed together and it was nearly disastrous. My father loved his motorbike, but my mother only loved my father. She balanced on a cushion behind him, as there was no pillion seat, and bounced off the back as he raced over a humpbacked bridge. He continued for three miles before he realised she was not there, and returned to find her red-faced and angry, sitting on the bridge. She adored my Father; gradually her anger subsided into sulks and then into a strange noble martyrdom that my father never took the time to understand – but the motorbike was sold.

I still have a large sepia photograph on my wall. They sit on the Ariel motorbike, a handsome, smiling couple; beautifully dressed and perfectly matched, and I look at the pillion cushion and smile that same smile.

My father loved his red Morgan car with the thick leather strap around the bonnet, but he crashed it in a ditch. My mother was horrified, but so relieved by their lack of injuries that she took a photograph of him sitting in the wrecked car, smiling my smile again.

She was more horrified by the extra hours she had to spend at the sewing factory, pedalling off in the dark and back home in the dark to an empty, lonely, silent cottage, deserted by my father, who was also working extra hours on the railway earning the money for their dream: his farm. She loved my father, but she hated the dark.

It was more than hatred; it was real fear. She was terrified of being alone. Brought up in a family of seven in a small terraced house in

13

the familiar back streets of Crewe, she knew only the reassuring night sounds of the shunting steam engines. Snorting and clunking their reassurances, these predictable friendly giants pierced the night with their whistles; hopeful eternal guardians of the town.

She had grown up with her argumentative and giggling sisters and wayward brother; her quiet Welsh father and her dominating mother. This was her life's blood and now it was draining away, seeping into the grey silence of the cottage with its damp walls and faded furniture.

One night, alone in the house, she heard a gentle tapping on the front door. Fear froze through my mother's veins, and as the tapping became more persistent, she began to scream, silently at first, for no sound would come out. It was as if the silence had claimed its victim.

My father returned from his nightshift to find her soaked in the real sweat of fear, huddled in the corner of the room, whimpering like a small child. My mother loved my father but she hated the cottage, the countryside, and the dream farm. The cottage had to go.

Now my father was faced with a real dilemma. How could this have happened, when he had planned so carefully? He had worked hard, saved money, provided a secure home, and made no hasty decisions. He had controlled and safeguarded all their dreams, and yet he was left at the beginning of their life together with the woman he loved, the woman who shared his dreams and ambitions, the woman whom he had made his wife, and the woman who was now crumpled and crying in the corner of the silent cottage.

I think that the grey ghost moved inside him then for I could still sense his remembered fears when he told me this story many years later.

My mother was gathered up warmly, the fire was lit, all the lights were switched on and they welcomed the dawn together, sipping hot tea. He'd made jokes about the tapping on the door. It had been frogs in the wet porch leaves – how strange – frogs; probably searching out insects. They laughed together about these frogs and he'd make more jokes about the invasion of the 'terror frogs' attacking my mother. She laughed because she loved him, not because she found it funny. They did not share the same sense of humour.

He filled all the vases with flowers and tried to give her back some of the things she loved, but he knew it was over. The flowers died; slumped, unarranged.

My mother and father moved out of the cottage.

He told me that he walked down my grandmother's path, stood at the gate and pointed towards a half-built house at the end of the street. "I shall buy that house," he'd said "and then they can stand at their gates and wave to each other."

And so they did, for over 50 years, until my grandmother's death at the age of 92.

My mother loved 100 Ernest Street, a semi-detached brick-built house with a pebble-dashed front. Like all its neighbours, it had a yellow and green privet hedge and was painted green and cream.

My father called it 'Dovedale', for that was where they had loved to go on the old Ariel. He had a wooden sign made and fastened it to the house. My mother was secretly embarrassed by this, as no other house had a name, but she allowed him this romantic notion.

The house was her true love and she heaped attention on it. Everything gleamed, and she spent her life shopping and polishing. She no longer went out to work because she was a wife, and, as my grandmother quickly pointed out, not one other wife in the street worked. It was considered a sign that her husband could not afford to keep her, or worse – that there was something wrong in the marriage.

My mother was a homemaker. She even arranged newspapers across her new green carpet like stepping-stones until one day my father grew angry, tearing them up and shouting; fading memories stirring in his heart of Dovedale and the days when they had danced over the river on real stepping-stones. My mother was puzzled. She had never seen him like this and she scurried up the street to talk to her mother and reaffirm her beliefs about real married life. Then she would return and arrange flowers even more fiercely, forcing them into unnatural shapes.

My father spent more time at work and on his allotments. Here he created two worlds, one of which I was later to share.

But my mother was nearly forty years of age and had started looking in prams. They had decided not to have children for reasons my father had never explained. All she knew was that he had some very deep fears rooted in the genes of his family, something he could not pass on to his children; something she'd never dared to discuss.

She was full of hope and became even more perfect, glowing, attentive, reassuring. Her adoration of my father shone through her pretty face, transforming her into the woman who'd danced on the stepping-stones. She spent less time with her mother, and seemed to be listening to him again. They bought a Ford Eight car – BTD78 – and vanished off on camping holidays.

I have the photographs; my mother in a shapeless woollen bathing costume, a bathing cap on her head, her arms outstretched in an expression of delight as the seawater laps round her ankles. (My mother hated deep water and never learned to swim.) My father, in an equally shapeless costume, is sitting high on a rock, laughing down at my mother, who he said was dancing a funny dance to make him laugh. One beautiful photograph shows them sitting side by side, leaning slightly towards each other, isolated in silent, hilly countryside. "How did you take it" I would ask my father, "when there were no people about?" "Look for the cotton," he'd say, and each time I'd search excitedly for the thread that ran from his fingers to the Kodak camera wedged into the facing rocks.

My mother became pregnant. That war had broken out was a far less important event. They had decided to have one child but my mother grew enormous. My grandmother and aunty Cissie took over her care as my father was working long wartime hours in the blackout. Having babies was not part of a man's world.

And so it was that we were born under the stairs in what my grandmother called 'the glory hole'. My sister arrived first, promptly at 4 o'clock in the afternoon – fat, contented, uncomplicated, and leisurely. My aunty Cissie, who had never been able to have children, claimed her as her own, a baby with thick black hair and an uneven, dreamy face.

Then they all waited and nothing happened. My grandmother started to worry, and the doctor and specialist were sent for. I had twizzled round and was no longer standing on my head. I used to think that my sister had kicked me and sent me spinning round in her determination to get out first. I was delivered straight onto my feet at 4:20, an identical birth weight to my sister. I had a wide, completely bald head, and I screamed myself into the world and into my mother's arms and heart.

17

Blackout curtains shuttered every window of every house. Crewe, a vibrant railway junction, was a main target for German bombs. As the war rolled across our town, my father travelled through the night on the footplate of his steam engine. It was a world he knew well. When he came home, he entered a whole new world, one that continued to evolve, long after the war had ended, and one where his unspoken fears would continue to unravel.

Not Going To Die

My grandmother had deep-set, dark grey eyes, and millions of wrinkles. When I was very small I would sit on her knee and spread these wrinkles, pushing my fingers into their furrows, and move them about on her warm brown face. She would laugh and tell me how naughty I was, but I knew she never meant it.

She loved my twin sister and she liked me very much. Knowing that I was my mother's favourite child, she heaped love on my sister and food into me. For nineteen years we ate our meals in her kitchen. There, sitting on the chair I'm sitting on now, we enjoyed her wonderful cooking.

I had never been interested in food in my own home and my mother worried about this. In a desperate effort to fatten me she created a 'shop' on the metal kitchen cabinet. She would pull its rusted leaf down and arrange small drab portions of food on little plates. Then she would coax me in from my play in the garden and conduct a strange ritual. Pushing pennies and half-pennies into my hand, she would stand opposite me describing the dreadful food in a wildly excited false 'sales lady' voice, and, embarrassed, I would buy it with her money and try to swallow it to please her. I remember staring at the cabinet's rusted hinges and tasting the rust with each swallow. I remember paying too much for everything in an effort to end the game and get back into the sunshine, and I remember feeling the despair and sadness in her, and my own sinking sense of failure. I carried these feelings out into the sunshine where they ate their way into my games.

My grandmother's kitchen was wonderful. Remarkably, in times of ration books and careful eking out of butter, meat, and cheese, we dined like kings. Warm colourful, loud, and loving, the food spilled out from the black lead stove. Giant sausage-shaped puddings unrolled from cloths. Full of currants and called Spotted Dick, they provided my twin and me with a daring chance to shock our mother as the word 'dick' entered our giggling conversation at every opportunity. Huge joints of beef were basted and gave up dripping fat with its enviable brown bits, and rice puddings, thankfully stuck to their enamel dishes that I'd then be allowed to scrape.

We sat at the table and ate until we were too full to move. We were never given too much to drink. Tiny glasses containing only a mouthful of Tizer or Dandelion and Burdock, bought from a man with a van, were rarely refilled. I never understood whether the meanness with drink was based on my grandmother's carefulness, or had spilled over from her strongly voiced beliefs about the dangers of alcohol. In my grandmother's house, food was a sensual celebration, and drink, of any sort, was a sin.

My mother and my aunt helped prepare these meals, simply doing as they were told. Neither of them could cook, which was strange, as my mother had a family to feed, and my aunt a whole hospital. I would sometimes visit her in the kitchen of the hospital, where, amazingly, she was known as the head cook. She would stand at a huge sink surrounded by metal trolleys with metal boxes and send these off to various parts of the hospital according to their labels. No one ever complained, and all the doctors, nurses, and patients were fed by the time she took off her white overall, pulled on her coat, and cycled home. She never talked about food, smelled of it, nor showed any interest in it. I supposed that if people were ill or very busy they wouldn't even notice what they ate, and I think my aunt thought so too.

After our meals, my grandmother would clear the dishes and her daughters would wash them. My sister and I would be fatly banished to the bottom of the garden, and my grandmother would have a 'lie-down' on her couch. This hard brown couch was in the kitchen next to the fire, and above it, on the wall, were two photographs of soldiers. One was my aunt's twin brother, Philip, pale-eyed and handsome; the other showed a young, dark-haired soldier with deep-set grey eyes. This was William, the son who had died in the First World War. Once, I was allowed to sit at the end of the couch as my grandmother lay there. She told me how William had lied about his age and enlisted to fight at the age of seventeen. A year later, she had received a parcel containing his uniform and the contents of his pockets. A hole pierced the tattered cloth where the bayonet had pushed through and killed him, and a hole remained in her heart until the day she died. Uncle Philip had returned from the war, but, although she heaped affection on him, he was never her well-loved son, and his own son, young Philip, was completely ignored by my grandmother, as if in some strange punishment or revenge.

My grandfather lived in this house, too. (Uncle Philip looked exactly like him.) Tall, thin and pale with watery blue eyes, he was Welsh, read the bible, and hated me. He flinched when I fidgeted and danced round the room, and winced when I sang and asked questions. Once, I poked my finger deep into a hot, sand-castled syrup pudding, and screamed out in pain, but the punishing stare from his faded cold eyes burned me far more deeply than the hot syrup. A silent man, full of thoughts, he frightened me. He could speak fluent Welsh, but never within my hearing. He adored my sister and even let her sit on his chair. I think he spoke to her in Welsh and I always remember plucking up enough courage to demand he speak to me too. I could feel the anger in him as he walked silently out of the room.

And then he became ill. For many weeks the whole house smelled of his cancer, and my mother, aunt, and grandmother scurried silently into the parlour where his bed was placed. They carried hot water and clean cloths, and I sat at the bottom of the stairs, next to the

21

parlour door, waiting for something to happen. They walked in to nurse him with pleasant expressions and as they came out carrying the sodden flesh-smelling cloths, their faces crumpled in pain.

Eventually, I stayed out of the way at the bottom of the garden, until, one day, after my sister and I had arrived for our dinner, we were guided into the next-door neighbour's kitchen. This neighbour wore very thick glasses and made us eat hard bread-and-butter pudding. Even though she was gushingly kind, it felt like a punishment for which we'd committed no crime. My sister grew silent and sullen for days, and when we were finally allowed back into our grandmother's kitchen, the smell of the cancer had gone. Warm love and syrup puddings had returned, and our grandmother was cheerful again. Our aunt pushed her bike into the shed and propped it once more against the mangle, cursing the bike chain, which was forever coming off, and my mother was patiently pale and polite.

Only my sister remained sad. She took me down the garden and told me that our grandfather had died a whole week ago, and no one had told me in case I became too upset. Everybody else knew, even the neighbour who had made us eat bread-and-butter pudding to cheer us up. I mourned the lack of truth but I never mourned my grandfather.

My grandmother always wore a long black skirt and lovely cream blouse, thick lisle stockings and black laced-up shoes. A thin gold cross hung from her neck, and a neat brooch smartened the lapels of her blouse. She placed a wide-brimmed hat on her head when she took me shopping. It was secured with a long, sharp, deadly looking hatpin, which, according to my aunt, could be used for stabbing male attackers. I could never imagine anyone daring to attack her.

Filled with equal amounts of love and hate, she was my protector. She smelled of fresh soap and whatever she was cooking. She made butter in a little machine, and drank the buttermilk or poured it over her potatoes to give her 'extra strength to fight the war', and she lived within a rigid routine that no one dared disturb. She appeared to hate all 'foreigners', and frightened me with tales of how she would slit the throat of any German soldier who parachuted into her garden. My belief that she would do it was reaffirmed one day when I ran in excitedly to tell her that I'd found a mouse playing in the bottom of the washtub. I took her hand and dragged her into the shed, and as I stood, delighted to share my find, she lifted a hammer from a nail on the wall and smashed it down on the whiskery creature, splattering it all over the sides of the tub. "Now I shall have to wash that out" was all she'd said.

But I loved her. She appears in my thoughts uninvited and often. She is sitting on my garden bench, shelling peas. She looks up, smiles, and says, "Where's your sister?" Or, she is sitting by my fire winding her long thin strands of hair around metal curling pins. It is then I remember her last words "Bring me my curlers. I'm not having the doctor see me like this." Then, suddenly, she announced, "I'm not going to die" and died before the doctor arrived.

Looking For Angels

"I'm going to church today," said the grandmother.

The child didn't look up. He was arranging his battle scene all over the living room.

"Just thought I'd have a look round."

The attackers balanced on the sofa; the enemy marched below them, hiding amongst the cushions. Some were already lying on their sides.

"Haven't been for years. You can come if you like?"

The battle was building up now. Tiny figures charged across the room and hit the floor. Guns exploded; planes zoomed low, skimming the carpet, and the dog ran into the other room.

"You don't have to come. I'm going anyway. You see, there's no one in there. They're doing it up. There's ladders and scaffolding all over the place."

Shouts; screams; smoke from under the sideboard. Clashes; crashes and thumps; gunfire down the sides of the chairs; quick darting movements --- then, silence.

"It's over," announced the child, standing up, and then, arms in the air, "We won."

"Good. Well done. Do you want a drink before we go out?"

"Please." He scooped some bodies up off the floor and stared at them. "Where are we going, Nan?"

"I'm going into the church. They're cleaning the angels. Do you want to come?"

"Yes; ok. Can I bring some soldiers?"

Brown Tweed Jacket

There has never been a time when I could not remember my father. At first it was the warm earthy smell of him, a scent I still desperately try to breathe as I push my face into his brown tweed jacket that still hangs in my wardrobe years after his death.

I take the pen out of his top pocket and stare at it, trying to imagine its last words, and I pry into every pocket corner and every dusty lining crevice, searching in vain for a memory; just one more memory.

Memories take his jacket from behind the back kitchen door with wide brown hands, and it is across his strong, square shoulders and wide chest. I look into his clear blue eyes, crinkling with humour or distant with worry, and I remember his straight nose, high cheekbones, and full, sensitive mouth.

Strangely, the 'memory eyes' are brown now, a reflection of my own, but his hair is thick and wavy, then streaked with grey, then white but always slightly frizzy, and smelling of outdoors and wet sheep. His moustache is stiff and handsome.

"You think you look like Clark Gable, Dad, with that moustache," I'd teased, and he laughed because someone once told him he did.

He had a lovely laugh and straight white teeth, one with a gold filling. Years later his gold tooth was extracted and placed in a small bureau drawer with a white elephant and a gold key.

"You never know when you might need to sell it," he said, and long after his death, to my shame, I did sell it. My children were small and I had very little money. It was as if he'd come to my rescue, and

I know he would have smiled, but I felt like Judas, and have always regretted it.

My father loved my sister and me. As we grew older he spent more time with us. Believing that babies lived in 'women's worlds', he waited until the magical age of three, and then began to take us out individually. The times I remember being with my sister and my father were rare, and usually planned as a surprise. He would meet us out of school, the pockets of his mac fatly packed with sandwiches, for he would buy nothing from cafes, and we would use up our 'quarter fares' and free passes granted to all engine drivers in Crewe.

The steam engines would breathe noisy grey breath over us, and we'd be welcomed onto their footplates. Everyone knew my dad and many wanted to talk to him, but when he was with us, he talked to us alone. He never stood and gossiped like my mother and grandmother. He never repeated the same conversation, as they did, and I never grew bored. I was often surprised, or worried, or delighted, but I was never once bored.

As we walked along the railway platform one day, an old engine driver shouted at a young cleaner about the untidy length of his hair. Waiting passengers were enjoying the young man's embarrassment, until, without slowing his step, my father let go of my hand, reached out, lifted the driver's hat to show his bald head shining clean and pink above his grimy face. The hat was immediately replaced as we strode off down the platform.

Other people told me stories. He had formed the Engine Drivers' Assurance Fund, and, unable to bear the frustration of working with a committee, he had once slid off his chair at an Annual General Meeting, crawled under the long table, and bitten the chairman's leg. On another occasion, elated after fighting a successful insurance claim for an injured driver, he celebrated by racing up the station escalators in the wrong direction, only to be confronted by two railway policemen keen to know why this respectable grey-haired man with a briefcase was behaving in such a peculiar way.

All my life, stories like these filtered through to me, but the father I knew wore the brown tweed jacket in winter and the pale cream dusty one in summer.

"You ought to be ashamed of those old coats," scolded my mother one day. "Throw them out – or I will."

She even dared to do it once. She hid the old cream jacket in a plastic bag and put it in the dustbin. As he retrieved it and returned it to its rightful peg, I remember him saying "Leave my things where they are, Mrs Dustbin." and, forever after, he would occasionally call her Mrs Dustbin, especially when she was putting on her posh voice, the voice that made me blush with embarrassment.

One day, when I was walking alone along the main shopping road in Crewe, I saw my father on the opposite pavement. Suddenly, he started to run, as if in slow motion, his arms outstretched, towards my mother, who was approaching, laden with shopping bags. She stood, unable to flee in her panic, a grey-haired lady clutching bags from the Co-op. He crashed into her, and as the bags fell to the ground, he enveloped her in a passionate stage embrace, bending her struggling stout body backwards until she seemed to almost touch the pavement stones. I remember seeing her plump legs kicking as she struggled to regain her balance, and I remember the yellow oranges rolling into the gutter, but I remember no more, for I turned and ran down a side street, eager to pretend I knew neither of them.

When I was very small he made me a metal seat that he fastened onto the back of his bike. He said that it was just for me, and that I must always remember to stick my feet out, well clear of the wheel spokes. He'd strap me into it and wheel me out through the front gate. Kicking off from the pavement's edge, we'd leave our house and travel away, wobbly at first, but soon smooth and fast into the unknown, with me clinging tightly to his brown tweed jacket. I would close my eyes, feel the air rush past me, and know that I was flying. I'd stick my feet out and dare to lean back, never once letting go of my father.

We'd visit men with pigeons and ferrets, and sit and talk until it was dark. They'd pat me on the head and give me boxes of 'rubbish' out of their sheds. I loved 'rubbish', and soon they began to smile, as my constant reply to "Is there anything you want?" became "Have you got any rubbish?"

Then we'd fly back in the dark to face my mother's grumblings. "George, you shouldn't be keeping her out until this hour." and "Now where have you been?" She always wanted to know things.

I had just turned three. I remember my age because I had a constant reminder in my sister, travelling along through life twenty minutes before me.

"You're too little to be on that bike, Jill Madden." said older Maureen Riley peevishly. "I'm four, and I don't go out like that Er-er."

I never knew why she ended all of her sentences with the long triumphant "Er-er", but I always repeated the sound at the end of my replies, thinking that it must be a rule when talking to her.

"Well, I'm three Er-er," I chanted in the same singsong voice, and, pointing at my sister proudly, added "and so is she Er-er. So we're six Er-er. So there Er-er."

I marched off, an arrogant winner, secretly pleased that I'd got enough fingers to add up the sum, and very relieved that her silence meant I'd added it correctly.

One of the loves I shared with my father was a strong feeling for animals and everything natural. He had two allotments and it was there I kept my pigeons and ferrets. He grew all our vegetables and we ate eggs from our own hens. After the war, this was real luxury. We always ate well. One long shed full of hens was ruled over by a small angry cockerel called Nasser-Satan. He would fly at you from every angle. My sister refused to collect the eggs. She armed me with a dustbin lid and a big stick and pushed me into the hen cote. Then I would do battle with Nasser whilst trying to collect the eggs at the same time. She would stand outside with her fingers in her ears so that she couldn't hear him pinging off the dustbin lid until she let me out of my prison covered in egg yolk and hen muck.

I have many memories of my father's allotments, some of them sad. One day when I was about eight, a telegram boy on a bicycle rode up to our house and handed my mother a yellow envelope. She opened it fearfully, read its contents silently, and instructed me to run to the allotments and deliver it to my father.

I knew it was private but as I ran along the pavement and turned in to the privacy of the 'backses', I also knew that I must read it. "Brother Joseph died Deva Hospital." I was puzzled. I folded it carefully into its own creases and raced on. As I handed it to my father, I was no longer worried. I knew that it had been sent to the wrong person, as my father hadn't got a brother named Joseph.

30

I watched him read it, and, to my amazement, his eyes filled with tears. I stood staring in disbelief. He waved me away with an almost angry gesture. I walked slowly to the allotment gate, but as I turned, I saw my father leave his digging and sit down on his wooden bench. Then, instead of crying, he lifted his face to the sky and howled like an animal. My father was howling at the sky for a brother he hadn't got. I turned and ran down the backses, the strange, painful howling still in my head. Neither my mother nor my father mentioned the telegram again.

Years after their deaths, I found Joseph's death certificate. He was my father's eldest brother, named after my grandfather, and he had died in the Deva mental hospital.

As I grew older, I began to realise that was my father was more complicated than I'd first supposed. I once looked through four photograph albums, searching for a picture of me. Eventually, unable to find a single photograph of me, or my sister, I grew angry and suspicious.

"Dad, where am I in your photographs?"

"They were all taken before you were born," he explained.

"Well, what are you and mum there for?" I'd argued. Until that moment, I'd really believed that my parents were on earth for the sole purpose of having me. Seeing their albums changed everything; from then on, life became more complicated.

My father said that I was a 'butterfly' and that my sister was a 'plodder'. Plodders were safer than butterflies. Looking back, I realise that my father had tried to tether my dreams on several occasions.

One day, when I was about seven, I ran down our path to investigate my newts in the garden pond, and found not newts, but great big fish. There were at least twenty of them fighting for air, heads above the surface, mouths half-open; big golden-brown scaly fish with misty eyes. I backed slowly away and turned and rushed into the street. I shouted names and banged on doors, gathering every child I knew. "Follow me. Follow me." I screamed, and they did, in a noisy procession, my excitement spilling over onto them.

Shouting and whooping, we charged down the path, stopping at the edge of the lawn. I made them silently circle the pond, and just as we all gazed at the golden fish and I began to tell them my story, my father appeared in the doorway of his shed. His stern presence made them uneasy. They began to shuffle nervously as he approached. Determined to salvage my moment of glory, I raised my voice and exaggerated my discovery. As I described the foaming, writhing creatures, my father leaned forward and slowly picked each fish up out of the water. Each gaping head was stuck onto a stick, like a lollipop. He gathered them and held them like a bunch of flowers. They were kippers. One boy started to snigger, then another, and the infectious mocking quickly spread until the entire gang of children was laughing. They sauntered off, shouting rude things to me.

I stood on one side of the pond and my father stood on the other. He held out the bouquet of fishes to me in a mock romantic gesture. "You are a horrid man." I screamed. It was the first time I'd called my father a 'man' and it was the worst insult I could think of.

"Are you the Jill Madden whose aunty was murdered?" asked a friend's mother when I was ten.

"No," I said, automatically.

"Did your father live in Chambers Street?" she persisted.

"Yes." I felt a strange sense of doom.

"Then you are her – the Jill Madden whose aunty was murdered." She seemed almost pleased.

I worried about this for weeks. This was real, and I wasn't supposed to know. I stared at my sister, wondering if she knew. I tested her out, casually introducing murder into the conversation, questioning her about how she would feel if she knew a murder victim. She told me I was morbid. She didn't know. This made me feel even more alone.

A Madden woman had been murdered. Why? Was I like her? I felt frightened, and the more I thought about it, the more I convinced myself that eventually I would be murdered, too. All I had to do was grow up; then I'd be murdered.

I couldn't sleep; I ate even less than usual, and I didn't want to go outside. I didn't dare ask my father as it was his secret, and my mother's lack of discretion made her a risky person to confide in.

Only once more in my life had I felt this sense of doom. That was when I'd pieced together fragments of the *News Of The World* in the outside lavatory at my grandmother's house. It told a strange story of a woman who'd turned into a man. I'd had to pull the papers off a string behind the door and parts of the story had holes in it, but nevertheless it had made a deep impression on me. Within weeks I was convinced that I was changing sex. I examined myself fearfully. Yes, I was growing other parts.

Cold fear swept through me. How could I explain to my sister that she'd end up with a twin brother? How would my mother survive the ordeal of embarrassment, and the neighbours' gossip? I wanted to die.

I didn't die, but I did go on changing. In desperation, I searched for the cause, and for some strange reason, became convinced that it was because once, when I'd climbed up a ladder, my uncle had looked up my skirt and seen my knickers. The sex change was my punishment.

The fear was only dispelled when, after much thought, I realised that I was changing not from a girl to a boy, but from a girl to a woman.

All this changing, all this fear, and then a sad, sudden end – murder.

I ran crying to my mother and asked her about my dead aunt. Yes, she had been murdered.

"Don't ever talk about it to your father."

"Why was she murdered?" I needed to know.

"It happened in New Zealand a long time ago. I don't know why."

The fear stayed with me. Throughout my father's lifetime, it was never mentioned, but even now, the sad, silenced fears of my ancestor whisper to me in my dreams.

My father always believed that good health was one of the most important things in life. He didn't smoke and rarely drank, unlike his father, Joseph. My grandfather enjoyed a drink, gambled on the horses, constantly smoked a pipe, and was totally without ambition.

When I was three, I remember meeting him; a small white-haired, smiling man who smelled of tobacco and looked like Father Christmas. He had been a platelayer on the railway, and on his retirement, he travelled out to the village of Tilstock to help two maiden aunts run their small farm.

My father told me the story of how my grandfather had angered them by refusing to wear a best suit on a Sunday. Frustrated by their failed attempts to smarten him up, they had a green tweed suit handmade in Chester, and they insisted that he wear it on the following Sunday. He did; to their horror, he brought the cows up, did the milking, and cleaned out the entire shippon wearing the suit.

They never forgave him until the day he died, up a ladder picking apples in their orchard at the age of seventy-three, of a heart attack.

My father always believed that a heart attack would claim him, too, but, ironically, his genes nurtured the illness that had killed his mother. A cancer grew inside him for two years, and his strength began to fail. He told no one, but eventually became so weak that he asked me to go with him to the local hospital.

They made him sit in a wheelchair and as I pushed him along the corridors his expression was proud and resigned. He took no medication and he made two requests of me.

"Jill, when I am too ill to speak, do not let your mother give me medicine. I've known what it has been like to live, and I want to know what it is like to die. And, do not let your mother bring the vicar to see me."

And then, he talked about Dorothy.

Dorothy was the daughter of the head gardener at Betley Hall. She was slender and olive-skinned, with laughing brown eyes and a wide full-lipped mouth. He loved her, and when he was courting my mother for those long years, he was also courting Dorothy.

At night he would ride out of Crewe on his motorbike and as he approached the silent village of Betley he would switch off his engine and glide down to the edge of the wood. There he would hide his bike in the ferns and walk through the trees in to the grounds of Betley Hall. On one occasion, he startled a poacher who yelled out and vanished, terrified, into the night. I still have a newspaper cutting that describes the ghost of Betley Hall, a knight in armour emerging from the wood and floating in the mist toward the walled garden.

Dorothy would wait for my father in the walled garden and they would lie on my father's leather motorbike coat, secretly, under the stars – meetings forbidden by her father, and secret from everyone else until my grandmother found out.

Fate cruelly sent the local postman from Crewe to work in Betley for a month, and on his return, he told of how he'd seen my father leaving the village in the early hours of the morning. There was an immediate confrontation.

"Are your intentions towards my daughter honourable? If so, you have a decision to make."

Faced with the dilemma of destroying my loyal, devoted mother, and risking his future with the bright, vivacious, laughing Dorothy, he made the decision never to see Dorothy again.

He kept his promise.

But he always loved her, and on his deathbed, he talked to me about her, and asked me always to keep the leather coat, as he had done.

It hangs beside his brown tweed jacket in my wardrobe.

The Wardrobe Mistress

She had her back to me, and in the half-light it was difficult to recognise her. I stood silently watching as she opened the wardrobe door and rippled the clothes, stroking their edges; her long fingers plucking at the fabrics, sensually squeezing the cloth into fists; she pushed her face deep into their folds, breathing life into them; long sighing breaths of recognition.

The bedroom was no longer mine. She reclaimed every inch, every crevice; the bed was hers again. Her whole life hung in the wardrobe, and she had returned to live it.

Carefully, she slid a pale green dress off its hanger, pressed it against her slim brown body and smiled. She knew that he would love its primness, its freshness; it was a 'holding hands' dress, and she was ready to hold his hand.

'The Husband' would touch her gently, carefully, respectfully in the green dress. Nothing could go wrong.

"Please don't wear that; I know where you're going. Please don't go. Put it back in the wardrobe."

My voice cut through the silence; she wasn't startled. She turned, stared at me, unmoved by my outburst. Slowly her expression softened with recognition.

"May I have a glass of water?"

When I returned with the water she had gone. I tugged open the wardrobe door and searched frantically through the clothes. The green dress had gone with her.

By the time we met again it was too late. Weeks had passed and, disturbingly, several outfits had vanished from the wardrobe; small items at first - a black suspender belt that had been pushed to the back of the shelves, long velvet gloves with fingers full of memories, a black basque which had long ago failed to fasten on its third set of hooks and eyes.

Why was I keeping these things anyway - as mementos, or worse, as trophies? Why should it matter? But it did matter, especially when the Burberry trench coat left its hanger.

We needed to talk. I had to let her know that she had stepped out onto a path that was years longer than the 'green dress' path of the woodland walk.

When 'The Husband' had told her that his life had been empty until that moment and promised her a whole future of shared memories, he had meant it. I wanted her to understand that she'd have no one to share them with. I was the only person she might listen to. She was beyond the influence of her friends. She saw them as spiteful and envious. She was absorbed by her love for him, and already the 'husband' and his 'mistress' were cast in the star roles. His wife and family were shadowy figures of little consequence compared with this grand passion. The stage was set.

The next time I heard the hangers sliding along the rail, I burst into the room and quickly closed the door behind me.

"Now, listen to me."

I intended to be really assertive, but as she stood there in the slender black dress, curly hair piled high, with smiling brown eyes, I almost understood why she was doing this. She looked lovely. No wedding dress this; no wedding day. That had already taken place with the wife of 'little consequence'. This was her day.

"The Burberry mac incident didn't mean anything, you know." I spoke calmly.

Her eyes narrowed. "What do you mean, it 'didn't mean anything'?" She was angry now. "It may not have meant anything to you but it means everything to me. That was when he first promised never to leave me," she continued.

I remained silent.

"It was exciting. It was shocking and it was very funny. He was sat there in his local when I walked in, all high heels and smart Burberry, and sat opposite him. No one else knew what was under the coat. I can look very middle class when I want to, and anyway it's got nothing to do with you."

Hindsight gave me courage. "But you know it has."

She glared at me.

"Please return the clothes," I begged. "It isn't too late," I added, unconvinced.

"I shall not," she flared. "These are my clothes, this is my life, and," she hesitated, "I do not want to end up like you, a lonely old woman, all on her own."

The silence was charged; palpable. Neither of us dared to speak; then she was gone, leaving me in a bedroom full of memories.

For months I didn't see her. The house took on a strange, empty stillness. Her perfume no longer lingered on my pillows. The clothes in the wardrobe remained untouched, and every day, in every room, the silence deepened.

I thought I'd grown used to living alone but now I realised that her visits had warmed me. Her noisy, impetuous behaviour, her determination and hopefulness had filtered through my house like sunshine.

I wandered from room to room, switching lights on and off in a state of muddled desire for change. I rearranged plants, paintings, photographs and ornaments, desperate to stir some invisible magic into the still atmosphere and provoke a reaction. I played loud music, hoping to deafen the silence; I lit and re-lit welcoming candles, placing them in the night windows, but nothing changed. The waiting was suffocating.

How could this have happened? It was only an ordinary wardrobe, but it now took on a special power. I no longer dared to open it. As weeks passed I began avoiding the bedroom altogether, eventually, uncomfortably sleeping in the spare room. I closed her bedroom door and pretended it didn't exist.

As months went by I spent more and more time in the downstairs rooms of the house, gradually removing reminders of the past. Photographs turned their faces to the wall but the images, engraved by memory, stared out at me still. I destroyed them, slowly cutting them into confetti and throwing them into the air. They settled over the now dusty carpets and furniture.

In the effort to forget what was painful, I seemed to be forgetting everything. Mealtimes became a blur of vague hunger. Day and night intermingled, becoming one long half-light, stretching through past and present like a fading pathway. Numbed by an aching sadness, I sat silently in the darkened kitchen struggling to understand what was happening to me.

On this day, I felt oddly calm. Clearer thoughts penetrated the haze and I held on to these until I knew what I must do. Forcing myself to walk through the disordered rooms, I quietly climbed the stairs and opened her bedroom door.

At first it looked as if nothing had changed. I felt a strange mixture of relief and disappointment. Warily, I slowly opened the wardrobe door.

From somewhere, someone breathed a long sigh and the contents of the wardrobe seemed to sway slightly.

Tentatively, I reached inside and lifted out a pale grey designer suit. Holding it at arm's length, I studied its handsome Victorian-style jacket and beautifully pleated skirt, and smiled.

She had spent every penny she had on this suit, hoping to make a lasting impression on 'The Husband' and his friends at the formal dinner. His wife had feigned illness and refused to go. She knew this because he had told her. With a clear conscience, a beautiful suit, and fitted black boots, she stepped in as understudy and had a wonderful evening. "You really are doing her a favour," he had said, and she had believed him.

My smile spread wider still as I remembered this naiveté, and, holding the suit in my arms, I slowly began to dance in the empty room. Anger had faded long ago, sadness left only the faintest shadow, and grief finally spiralled away in the swirling, swaying rhythms of the past.

Out of breath now, I placed the grey suit on the bed and turned again to the wardrobe. Some of the clothes were missing. The tweed breeks and shooting jacket, checked green shirts and conker-coloured brogues with their tiny elegant tasselled laces, had left. The long, clingy animal-print dress with its beautiful necklace and matching print shoes had vanished, and the filmy pale-blue summer dress, bought especially for the holiday in Greece, was nowhere to be seen.

Totally absorbed now in the wardrobe world, I had not heard her come into the room; when I turned round she was already wearing the grey suit.

"Oh. I am so pleased to see you." I meant it.

Her apprehensive expression immediately changed and she grinned a wide, child's grin. "I was never going to speak to you again. I was determined," she blurted out. "I wasn't having you telling me what to do, telling me how to live my life." Her voice was no longer cross.

"I know," I said, simply.

"And when you started telling me what not to wear, I was furious." It was as if she needed to explain. "So I've been avoiding you, " she added.

"I know." I felt calm.

"On purpose." She almost stamped her foot.

I smiled, and, reaching into the wardrobe, I lifted out the long, slender, black leather boots and held them out towards her. "Here; wear these," I suggested tentatively. "They will look lovely with that suit."

"I know that." She almost snatched them. Sliding them on, she glanced up at me and, as if in apology, muttered, "I'm almost late, you see."

That night I slept soundly in my own bed with the wardrobe door slightly open. The summer light woke me early and I opened the windows wide. I had no desire to check the wardrobe.

Most of the day was spent in my overgrown garden. I'd never neglected it before and was surprised at how quickly the masses of healthy nettles had already strangled and suffocated the tiny, more sensitive plants. Without space and light the nasturtium seedlings had withered away. The yellow hop had thrived but in a fight for survival had throttled the new clematis, wound its rampant tendrils through gaps in the wooden shed door, moved in and died in the dark. Sadly, the leaking pond, always in need of water, had dried up entirely. Stranded hollow pond snails lay amongst its dusty pebbles.

I worked hard, determined to bring it back to life. I ate my meals there, in the sunshine, and by the time the evening borrowed the light, the plants could stretch and grow again. All week I worked outside and in the evenings I polished and tidied each room, rearranging furniture and filling the house with fresh flowers.

The kitchen sparkled. Never very interested in cooking, I now began experimenting with new recipes. Engrossed in the complication of balancing ingredients and soothed by background music I didn't hear her at first; the muffled crying, coming from the living room, grew louder and more insistent.

She looked thin and frail curled up amongst the sofa cushions. Dejection had replaced defiance. I didn't know what to say. She was the first to speak.

"He says he can't leave." She looked directly at me and began to sob again.

"Our house is nearly ready and he can't leave."

I remained silent.

"I had worked really hard, you see," she explained. "It is so beautiful. You have no idea how lovely it is." Her eyes smiled at the memory.

"I can imagine." I dared to interrupt.

"We found it together one day on a walk in the hills. It was derelict. All the stones were crumbling away." She laughed. "A tree was growing in the kitchen straight through the roof," she paused. "Sometimes birds perched in it." She was talking to herself now.

"We would hide in there in the dark and watch badgers. Oh, it was wonderful, high up on a hill looking down on the whole world. It was perfect." She hesitated. "We were perfect."

I looked at her, lost in her own world, living in her own dreams, suspended in an unreality so huge. I had no right to interfere. She sighed and looked down, twisting her hands together, curling up tightly like a frightened animal.

"Is there anything I can do?" It was a pointless question. She carried on speaking. "And the garden," she uncurled slightly. "It was huge and so beautiful". She looked up. "I spent months and months planting borders. The rabbits ate a lot of it – and the pheasants."

"Pheasants?" I questioned and this time she heard me.

"Yes, pheasants. I love them; they were everywhere. When I woke each morning they were calling out all over the garden and when I opened the door they ran along the stone walls to be fed." I was in the garden with her now.

"The house was in the middle of a shoot, you see. That's how we got it. I always went shooting with him, for years, until..." Her voice faded away and she changed the subject. "He's a builder. He did the cottage up just for us. We talked about it endlessly. He's so good at rebuilding things." She was full of praise.

"And then?" I questioned cautiously.

"Oh, then we moved in." She was triumphant now.

"He moved in with you?" I had to ask.

"Well, not exactly... no; the time wasn't quite right. He was there often and sometimes I prepared dinner and he'd cut the grass and we'd sit outside and drink wine and make plans," she paused, remembering. "We were always making plans," she smiled.

"And what about his family?" I dared to ask.

"Oh, he had to go home, but we talked about them a lot. We weren't silly. We were real. We knew it was going to be an awful shock when he left." She answered immediately now, much more sure of herself.

"They lived in my head for hours when he went home. I tried to work out how I could make him happy, and them and me, way into our futures."

"And did you?" I asked.

"Did I what?" she looked surprised.

"Did you work out how to make everyone happy?"

"Sometimes," she hesitated. "Nearly, very nearly, but it was hard. Feeling jealous was a problem and the waiting became difficult as well." She sank back exhausted. "Can I have a glass of water?" she asked quietly.

I thought about her a lot after that. Now that my thoughts were free from the nervous painful feelings, it became easier. She was no longer a place I avoided, in fact, quite the opposite.

To my surprise, I now enjoyed joining her in the stone cottage on top of the hill. I, too, watched the pheasants and remembered how one day two stoats, working together, hunted the walls, killing shrews and carrying them to their nest under the summerhouse.

One spring, I helped the gamekeeper lift the pheasant chicks from the incubators, and listened to the un-hatched eggs for signs of life. Any sound or movement meant I could crack the eggs and help the weak, sticky hatchlings emerge. They were good memories; in them the cottage grew warmer and more beautiful, the flower borders wilder and more natural. Giant hollyhocks, poppies, forget-me-nots, periwinkle and geraniums spread among the wild honeysuckles and ivies. The bracken thickened and became almost impenetrable. I flattened nests in it and lay, watching the buzzards watching me. I walked my dogs in the surrounding woodland and discovered where the badgers lived, and I stopped cutting the grass.

When I saw her again she looked older. At first I thought she was choosing her next outfit from the wardrobe. I walked quietly across the room and sat on the edge of the bed. She was replacing the black dress.

"I won't be needing that anymore." She was talking to the wardrobe. She slid it to the end of the rail. "Or that." The stretchy print dress joined it. "Or those," the shooting clothes, "or that, or that, or that." She sharply shunted the clothes in time with her words and firmly closed the wardrobe door. Then she turned, and, sighing, leaned against it to stare at me.

"Why didn't you tell me it would end like this?" --- a tired, accusing question.

I remained silent.

"You knew all along, didn't you?" she said, more angry now. "You could have saved me all this upset you know. I would have listened to you." but she was unconvinced.

"I tried," was all I could offer.

"I have spent years living his life instead of my own." She sat down on the other side of the bed, shoulders hunched.

"No, you haven't. You've spent years living your own life. Nothing has changed."

"Well it should have done. We planned it, we lived it and now he can't leave his wife. He must have known that from the beginning." She grew more angry.

"Why?" I asked. "None of us know things at the beginning."

"He said he would never leave me, he promised." She sounded like a child.

"And he's kept his promise. He hasn't left you. You've left him."

"Yes," she whispered, crying silently.

I wanted to tell her, that I'd never leave her. Instead, I stood up and walked slowly out of the room, closing the door behind me.

I never saw her again. The clothes still hang in the wardrobe, exactly as she left them. I do not look at them now. It was several years before I realised that the green dress had never been returned. She believed that wearing the green dress meant, 'nothing could go wrong'.

She was right.

Clothes in Summer

I never understood clothes in summer, when it was hot; when there were flowers, and the bracken fronds uncurled like furry insects and tickled my skin without asking.

I never understood shoes in summer, when the grass cooled the soles of my feet and the dew squeezed gently between my toes, sticky and sweet.

I never understood clothes in summer, when the bluebells pushed through the speckly leaf mould and welcomed my warm body that pressed the stemmed juices, as I rolled in the broken blue flowers and pushed my fingers deep into the moss, disturbing the sleeping midges.

Only then did I understand clothes.

Green Frog Blood

At the bottom of my Nanny's garden, through a hole in the hedge, lay a ditch thick with green frogs. Fat-fingered and mottle-skinned, they clambered over each other, half submerged in a seething mess of grey spawn. I loved them. Crouched for hours on a splintering plank, I stared down into their warm clumsy matings, amazed by the effortless power of the bloated mother frogs carrying their wrinkled mates, sucked dry yet still stuck firm with special suckers. Their croakings were deafening, throbbing in my head long after I had left the plank and returned through the hole in the hedge.

They reappeared in nightmares as alligators, silent and threatening, their gold slit eyes watchful, lying in wait for each member of my family, snapping them one by one from the plank in an explosion of green frog blood.

Each spring, these frogs became my obsession until one day, when I was twelve, everything changed. As I crawled back into the garden and stood up, I saw a young man in the yard outside my Nanny's back door. Puzzled, I stayed at the end of the path, dusty, hedge-speckled, and grass-stained, smoothing my frock and wishing I'd worn my socks. My Nanny never had visitors who weren't relations, yet there he stood, tall and very thin with dark auburn curly hair and pale skin. Strangely for a boy only a year or two older than me, he wore a suit, and it wasn't a Sunday.

I felt like the visitor as he waked towards me, and in panic, I almost dropped to my hands and knees to return to the frogs. Only the thought of my dignity and a possible sighting of my navy blue knickers stopped me. He stretched out his hand in a formal greeting and shook my grubby hand gently. "I am Jack. What's your name?"

"Jill," I replied, and felt very silly, and, for some reason, very angry.

This simple introduction was to resonate throughout both our lives. I don't remember revisiting the frogs and I never had the dream again.

"But who are you?" I asked nervously, and he explained that his father was courting my Aunt Cissie and had insisted on bringing him along to meet my grandmother.

I was horrified. They would have been in less danger if they'd walked the plank of my dreams. My fiercely possessive grandmother had battled every one of her daughters' men, and, losing one battle after another as they left to get married, she'd settled all her last hopes upon Cissie.

My mother had told me the story of Cissie's failed marriage to an unsuitable man who'd left Cissie because she couldn't cook, and of the thwarted attempts to smuggle pre-cooked dinners into her house to save her marriage. I went on to learn about Cissie's consequent illness and my mother's embarrassment and disbelief when she took Cissie to the hospital.

She explained, "When Cissie came out of the doctor's room she told me she had cancer, and I started to cry."

"Don't you dare cry, our Edie." shouted Cissie. "Get outside."

And, taking my mother by the arm, she'd marched her around the side of the hospital building. There, to my mother's amazement, frail Cissie had shouted and screamed and raged, kicking the wall, clenching her fists, and swearing words my mother had scarcely heard before. As my mother sobbed quietly, Cissie danced in anger and shouted disgraceful things to God, throwing herself at the rough brick wall, until she sank, exhausted, onto the pebble path at my mother's feet.

My mother reproached, "Come on, our Cissie – making a show of yourself. There's no need for that." whereupon Cissie had started to laugh. This frightened my mother even more, and she'd pulled my exhausted aunt to her feet, linked arms, and hurried her away to the bus stop.

Cissie had nearly died. A massive operation reduced her to a skeletal figure, nursed month after month by my determined grandmother, who, having brought Cissie back from the dead, claimed her as the eternal daughter, the daughter who would never leave.

"My father is going to marry your aunty, and I'm glad because I really like her. She makes us laugh." How simple this boy made it sound. Already influenced by his quiet voice and lovely gold-speckled eyes, I almost believed him. "I go to the pub with them and we just sit and talk."

It was then I knew I had to warn him. Suddenly, a strongly protective feeling overshadowed my shyness, and I felt sorry for this innocent boy and his naïve father. My grandmother banned alcohol and anyone who drank it. The only things she hated more were Germans, and Roman Catholics.

"I don't think you ought to mention the pub," I said. I quickly distracted him. "Come and see my sister's rabbit."

We walked to the end of the garden and stared into the hutch. My father had placed it in long legs so that it was at face height, and it housed a large grey chinchilla named Ernest Oliver Cecil Winston Percival James Madden, Esq. I'd punched the name out on a machine at Crewe railway station, spending a great deal of time getting all its letters right. The name was stuck to his door, which no one but my sister was allowed to open. She really loved this rabbit; unlike me, she had no interest in animals, and it was surprising that she loved Ernest with such passion and possessiveness.

Jack peered into the straw-filled hutch with amused interest, and the fat, expressionless rabbit stared back. Worried by what would be taking place in the back kitchen, I chattered nervously, poking dandelion leaves through the wire netting, until Ernest, irritated by our presence, thumped his feet and vanished in to his darkened 'bedroom', leaving us staring at an empty cage.

Jack smelled of soap and mothballs. He looked at me and smiled without showing his teeth, and golden freckles danced in his eyes.

I thought of his father walking the plank in my nightmare, followed by Cissie, and I almost saw the hungry alligators twitch.

My grandmother grew to hate Jack's father, and this hatred exploded one day in the back kitchen where they were first introduced. Jack and I were in the garden. We sensed the tense atmosphere and heard the shouting. I climbed onto the drainage pipe and looked through the window.

Aunty Cissie was crying, big Jack was shouting, and my grandmother, like a tiny angry devil, was dancing in rage. Suddenly, she rushed at him, and, jumping into the air and stretching to her full height, she slapped him, hard, across the face. "Get out of my house, you drunken Catholic," she screamed, "and take your son with you."

And he did.

Privet Hedges

We had a privet hedge. Every front garden in our street had one.

I tried to eat the leaves, but they were so bitter they made me feel sick. They stuck between my teeth and I couldn't spit them out. I tried.

"Stop spitting into my hedge or I'll tell your mother," shouted the woman next door. "Spit on your own hedge."

"What eats privet leaves?" I asked my best friend.

"Stick insects." She knew everything.

"What do they look like?"

"Sticks, of course, stupid." She laughed and ran off.

And then, I saw the advert.

I ordered hundreds of eggs. I had no idea of their size or where I would keep them. All I knew was that there were enough privet hedges in our street to feed a million insects. They wouldn't starve and no one need ever trim a hedge again.

The Road to the Doll's House

One of the best things about school was Mo. Tall, with golden ringlets bouncing on her shoulders she walked alone across the playground. Pale skinned and green eyed she strode on long legs, taller than everyone else, even the boys. She was able to fade into the background and become gently invisible, whilst other infants bobbed about like brightly coloured ping-pong balls in a fairground game.

Dressed immaculately in hand-knitted clothes, bright white ankle socks and well-made leather sandals, Mo towered above the others in every way. She said little, thought a lot, wrote beautifully in joined up writing and could play the piano in joined up music. It had always been my dearest wish to play the piano and I'd practised for hours on our sideboard and my school desk. I'd practised until my fingers were sore and my wrists ached and became so convinced that I was ready for a recital in front of the school that one day, despite my shyness, I'd volunteered to play.

Sitting on an itchy cushion at a real piano I played my tunes. On and on I went until the jangled noise was drowned by laughter from the other children and I was hurriedly removed from my cushion by Miss Jones. She took me on one side and pointed out my lack of musical skills in a kind voice and as my face grew red and tears ran down my cheeks I could hear Mo playing 'The sun has got his hat on', and all the children singing, 'hip, hip, hip, hooray'. She hadn't even needed a cushion.

I didn't understand Mo. She wasn't arrogant, she wasn't unkind but she was aloof in the manner of a cat. Puzzled, I told my mother about her and she explained that I'd known her before birth as Mo's mother and my mother had talked stomach to stomach at our garden gate and then Mo had been born, a very big baby, one month before me and my twin sister. This was fascinating. Had we communicated from the inside, yet curled up in our separate worlds? Had I known she was there waiting to be born, to be my friend, having arrived earlier to make sure everything was all right in case I lost my way? Did she know that my sister was in there too, so close yet much more distant? Had their rivalry started then? Was this why I knew I had to be her friend, her best and only friend?

I needed to be Mo's friend but I didn't know how to be it. We were so different; her tall, strong, elegant, clever and hard-working with long 'spun into gold' hair from the fairy stories; me thin with a mop of brown disobedient curls and sleeves pushed up on stick arms and legs too thin to hold my socks up, so that my mother made me wear garters under my purple strangled knees.

I loved Mo but my twin didn't even notice her. My sister became peevish and bullying whenever Mo was near. She scowled and jostled in the cloakroom daring to push in front of Mo, grabbed her own school mack first and trailed it on the dusty floor. Mo ignored this rude behaviour, fastened her neat coat with its stylish half-belt, and hoisted her leather hand-stitched satchel onto her back. Carrying her recorder and music in a neat flat folder, she strode out alone with me trailing yards behind her and arriving home late because I'd stood to watch her disappear over the horizon and then stood again to stare and wonder where she went.

"Oh no. You've forgotten your coat again our Jill. You'll catch your death." It seemed unlikely I'd catch my death because I couldn't catch a ball or our dog when he ran off but I knew with complete certainty that Mo could. I prayed that when Mo did catch it she'd share it with me.

Grown-ups used to tell us to take an apple for the teacher, and Pat Riddell did. She balanced the apple on top of her inkwell hole so it wouldn't roll off. It was a beautiful, large, shiny red apple straight out of the snow-white story and it stayed there all morning, glistening under florescent lights. The 'war was on' and we didn't see many apples then so she boasted with it all day, telling us about how she'd eat it for her lunch at afternoon playtime. She made sure that everyone stayed friends with her all day in the hope of getting some of the core. This apple wasn't for the teacher at all. It was just for ordinary Pat Riddell.

I don't know how it happened but as afternoon break began Mo and me and the apple were the only ones left in the classroom. The children roared outside and the room fell silent. We looked at each other and then at the apple and then, without saying a word, Mo picked it up, took a bite out of its side and handed it to me. Without hesitation I bit a hole in its other side. Silently we left the room and as I closed the door I remember seeing the white scars on the fruit and feeling so happy. We were friends. We were wrong but we were friends.

Pat Riddell screamed, shouted and cried until even I felt sorry for her. The white bites had turned a nasty shade of brown and the apple had lost its glamour. We all sat in silence as the teacher commanded, "Hands on heads."

Immediately obedient, every child sat rigidly upright, flattening heads onto shoulders with tightly clasped interlocked fingers. The boy in the desk next to mine turned white with the effort to be good, arching his spine in the shape of a back to front letter C, forcing his face to the ceiling and struggling to breathe. This was serious.

"Hands on heads", preceded fearful happenings. I never understood why we had to obey this strange command and I never knew how it helped us, or the teacher. Perhaps it was that hands were fiddly things, capable of getting up to mischief, capable of pinching, hair pulling, squashing or making rude signs but whenever we had to put them on our heads, trouble was on the way.

I held my head on and waited.

"No one goes home until I find out the truth. I shall ask each person to tell me if they bit the apple and you must tell me the truth. This is no longer about apples. This is about truth." I sat at the front of the room while Mo sat at the back. I was shaking and now my face matched the apple.

When innocent, I always looked and felt guilty for everyone else and this time I was in the wrong.

"Did you Jill Madden, did you?"

"No", I whispered.

"Louder", she demanded, leaning forward and staring into my eyes. I remembered my grandmother's words about how important the truth was.

"No", I shouted at the top of my voice. I waited to be struck down. I waited for the war to come through the window and pull me out by the hair. I waited.

"No, no, no", travelled around the room and I dared not turn round.

"I certainly did not", replied Mo with such certainty that the teacher almost apologised. And then it was over. Flossy Fletcher wet her knickers, Pat Riddell suddenly stopped crying and the teacher crashed the apple into the paper bin where it split into ugly squashy pieces. I felt sick, but our friendship was sealed forever and we walked home side by side in silence. I had entered a magical world alone. My twin was no part of this and I was glad. With Mo I was never a 'twin' and she was my first real friend. She chose me as a whole person, not half of someone else, the first person, big or little, who had ever done so.

Strangely I began to grow, like a plant moved from the half shade into the sunshine. I stretched out in all directions. My journeys to school became simple and short, no longer hampered by the essential ritual of touching every single garden fence post in our street. Missing one had meant a return journey in order to repeat the entire process and sometimes I would hear the school bell ringing the other children in.

I could now tread on as many pavement cracks as I liked without fear of 'marrying rats' and the little square gardens no longer had to score points out of ten before I could walk past them. This last ritual was a complicated time consuming job. It involved standing on walls, peering over gates, spying through and under privet hedges or jumping up and down on the pavement catching quick glimpses.

This jack-in-the-box approach drew concerned attention from a friendly neighbour who told my parents "there's something wrong with her". She had watched me 'walk' to school and convinced herself that I must be 'funny in the head'.

She'd warned me. "You're funny in the head you are. Get to school and stop being daft."

I'd accepted it as a compliment and dismissed it until she told my mother, who told my father. Amazed and puzzled by their reaction I tried to explain why I had to do these things but nothing comforted them.

Eventually it was decided that my mother would walk me to school, tightly holding my hand. I hated it. My hands longed for the touch of the friendly fence posts, my desperate feet dodged crevasse cracks and the gardens remained unscored. By the time she hugged and kissed me and pushed me into the long trail of queuing children, I was beside myself with anger and misery. The teacher welcomed us as we marched through the school doorway, arms stiffly by our sides, fingers pointed down, heads held high.

"Good little soldiers", she shouted. "Well done. Ten out of ten."

Then I met Mo and was invited into her world. Mo's house smelled of orange blossom and cats. I followed her through the living room into the kitchen where a heavy door hung with pinnies and cloths, swung open onto a back yard. Here a huge dog kennel was pushed up against a six-foot brick wall. A warm smell of dog rose from the blue yard bricks as the kennel shuddered and breathed. I loved dogs.

"That's our Peter. Have a look in."

Carefully I edged between the house and kennel and comforted by the warm snoring and my trust in Mo, I decided to crawl round to the entrance. My wellies squeaked on the pathway, gritty stones bit into my knees and a big splinter hooked my frock. I thought for a minute that someone was pulling me backwards until suddenly the splinter snapped, catapulting me head first through Peter's doorway. We met head to head.

Peter opened his eyes and stared straight into mine and from somewhere in the confined space I could hear his tail thumping a welcome on the floor. He was huge and black, the dog in one of my stories with 'eyes as big as saucers', he wasn't frightening and he liked me. A fat tongue reached out, licking my face.

"Hello", I whispered. "I'm Jill", but he seemed to know that already.

Mo's mother went out to work as a cook in a sewing factory. My mother had never been allowed to go out to work and I think that this mother was the first 'liberated woman' I had ever met. She never seemed to ask permission for anything and she laughed a lot. She made wonderfully decorated cakes, imprisoning them under glass domes on top of the piano where they were admired but rarely eaten. She vanished into a long secret pantry under the stairs and produced an abundance of food. In Mo's house food was a celebration. In ours it was a necessity. Irishmen from the cattle-market arrived with meat, vegetables and fruit I'd never seen before. There was no war in Mo's house and I ate all the time. The child unable to swallow food without real effort in one street became a food lover in the next.

In this kitchen we played unnoticed and unnoticing. We painted maggots for races, tried to gas earthworms when they were injured, melted gramophone records over a paraffin heater, created sculptures and best of all we moved into the doll's house together.

Mo's father built a large dolls' house. Kneeling down it was possible to peep into the bedrooms and bathroom. He created the house both of us wanted, a large middle-class house with an inside lavatory. Mo's lavatory was in a shed at the end of her garden and I sometimes wondered if this affected her choice of friends. We knew no one who lived in a real house like this. Instead of lino, neat, tasteful carpets fitted the floors. Tiny light bulbs lit every room, original paintings hung on the walls above elegant miniature furniture. On the table stood a tiny fruit bowl full of pea-sized fruits. As we kneeled side by side in worship we stared into another culture, another world and it stared back.

Decades later we remain friends. Her modern house is filled with warm bright colours, fresh flowers and one very large black and white cat. We talk endlessly and laugh a lot just as we always did.

My cottage is isolated. High on a hill, surrounded by trees, it looks over the Cheshire plain. Sometimes, in the early evening, I switch on all the lights and sit alone on the sandstone wall, which borders its gardens. I stare at the tiny-lit windows and white painted door, travelling back through time to join Mo kneeling in front of the original house. I walk silently up to the windows and peep in. Neat tasteful carpets fit the floors, lovely paintings hang on walls above elegant furniture and a large, black dog stretches out on the rug.

I know without looking into the kitchen that there is a bowl of fruit on the table.

Model mouse

He saw the mouse trapped behind plastic. It had babies, pale pink wormy creatures with no fur.

He tapped gently on their prison but they didn't move. Their mother stared with bead eyes and because she looked frightened he crept away.

That night he couldn't sleep, thinking about the tiny family struggling for breath.

Perhaps that was why he had an asthma attack in his nightmare.

"They'll suffocate", he spluttered.

"Who will?" his mother tried to calm him.

"The mice. They can't breathe, they don't have air. Get them out", he sobbed.

It was impossible to comfort him. When he walked to school the next day he visited the mice. They were still there, stiff and frozen, waxen and solid.

"They're dead." he sighed. His friend pulled him away.

"Don't be daft, they always were. Come on, we're late."

But it was a lie, yesterday they were breathing.

Neville Street

Thirty-five Neville Street was the centre of my world for many years. A pointed finger away from my own home; my grandmother's house was to play a crucial part in my life.

My twin sister and I walked to her house every day for our dinner and so Neville Street became our adopted street. Made up of semi-detached houses with small front gardens and wooden gates, we considered it not as posh as our street because the front doors were on the sides of the houses.

Opposite our house and on one side of Neville Street were two shops; Morton's and Riley's. They fiercely competed for custom as they both sold the same things and their owners were enemies. Mrs Morton was old and dusty like her shop and Mr Riley was smart and organised like his.

My mother ran screaming out of Riley's shop one day when she suddenly felt twitching movements in the lining of her coat. "I've got a mouse up my sleeve", she blurted out and hot with embarrassment and fear and red with anger at me, who'd lost the mouse the day before, she rushed into the back kitchen and threw the coat on the floor.

"If only I'd been in Morton's", she'd said. "I'd hate Riley's to think we'd got mice."

A large verandah, supported by two pillars, stretched over both shops and here we would play when it was raining. We swung round the pillars until we were dizzy and sat on the shop steps in the thunderstorms, counting between the distant rumblings of thunder and flashes of silver lightning.

"Only two miles away Jill Madden. I dare you to dance in the lightning", shouted Sean Riley. And I'd dance round and round in the warm rain until my frock stuck to my legs and my cardigan changed shape. I'd stretch out my arms and sing to the sky, feeling sorry for my poor aunt who I knew would be curled up and shivering with fear under my grandmother's table, praying for the storm to end.

Opposite the verandah, on the other corner of Neville Street grew nettles, dock leaves, brambles and tall grass. There in summer our gang built dens of corrugated iron and sat huddled together rubbing dock leaves into our nettle stung arms and legs. In winter we modelled hollow winter warmers out of clay, stuffed them with rags, lit them with forbidden matches and charged round holding them high in the cold night air, dreading our parents calling us in.

Every November we built a bonfire on this field and once, fearful of a rival gang, highly organised and made up of the entire family of fourteen children, we hollowed out our bonfire and hid inside to protect it from raiders. That year they crept up and set it alight. They were as terrified as us as we exploded from our bonfire like living fireworks.

At the top of Neville Street a large cattle market edged another field and every Monday my world was transformed with the auctions, which invited people and animals in from all over the country. On this day we would run frantically up and down the streets slamming the gates against flocks of sheep and herds of pigs who were supposed to snap our ankles off with one bite. Occasionally a panicking animal would smell blood from the nearby slaughterhouse, crash out of the cattle truck and stampede down the street.

One hot summer Monday I remember hopping over Neville Street's warm, dusty paving slabs chanting, "Tread on a crack and you'll marry a rat."

Concentrating fiercely, avoiding all pavement cracks, I tempted fate by skipping at speed. Believing that one miss-judged hop might throw my entire future into peril, I was deaf to the hysterical screams from the other children. "Cow escaped. Mad cow escaped."

"Tread on a crack and you'll marry a rat." My feet slapped rhythmically on the grey flagged pavement. Head down, faster and faster I hopped, as, head up, the terrified animal charged towards me.

"Cows are worse than bulls. They charge with their heads up and watch you," Maureen Riley had said and she knew because she had a big overgrown back garden behind her dad's shop where the poor crazed animals took refuge.

I remember the burning fear, the dusty dryness in my mouth, the loud screaming in the silent street and the rotten smell of wet flesh as the creature rushed towards and past me into Riley's back garden. I hadn't moved but now, flecked with its foam and sweat, I forced myself into the middle of the overgrown privet hedge and waited.

There, with the bitter taste of privet in my mouth, I watched the poor animal. Fear seemed to leave it then as it stood head down, perfectly motionless, in the long grass. A truck drove up, two red-faced cattle men jumped out and a cautious crowd gathered at the gate. I prayed for the cow to walk gently out with them. I silently begged it to act like a cow; chew its cud, swish flies with its tail, wipe its nose with its tongue; but the poor rigid animal pawed the ground and snorted and the men walked up and shot it through the head.

Slowly its legs crumpled and its heavy body slumped down in the blood-spattered grass. They tied it with ropes, hoisted it into the truck and drove off. The crowd wandered away.

I struggled out of the hedge and walked over to the flattened grass. I knelt down where the cow had fallen and stared at the red speckled daisies. Then I looked up at the sky accusingly, wondering angrily where God had been. The God who was supposed to know about every dead sparrow hadn't taken much notice of one big dead cow. I put my head down into the daisies and cried.

"You see, I was right Jill Madden er-er," shouted Maureen Riley from her back door. "Cows do charge with their heads up."

I loved Mondays. Driven out of the house by my mother's obsession with washing, I would spend hours in the cattle market. Here I felt special, unrelated to my family, a changeling child. I never remembered meeting my sister there. I reached up on my toes to pull on the fat whiskery lower lips of the shire horses. I stuck my fingers into the sloppy mouths of sucking heifers and I watched the handsome Irishmen charm the local big girls and their mothers, exchanging fresh meat and vegetables for kisses. Nothing in the market was rationed. People laughed, swore and peed in the street and no one told them off.

Marjorie, a strong, wild, handsome girl with thick yellow hair told rude stories and no-one was shocked. One Monday a cattleman asked Marjorie to bring him a length of rope. He promised to teach her something really special. She was so excited about this that she boasted it to the rest of us even though he'd sworn her to secrecy. "Have we got any rope for Marjorie to take to the cattleman?" I'd asked my mother who usually didn't listen to a word I said. What followed was a total surprise. I was questioned in detail and then my mother took her coat from behind the pantry door and buttoned it to hide her crossover piny. Collecting more mothers on the way she marched up Neville Street and in through Marjorie's front gate returning hours later, flustered, pink but triumphant.

"Marjorie won't be playing in the cattle market ever again."

What had I done? That night as I lay awake by my fat, warm sister, I thought of Marjorie imprisoned in the dingy grey house, the market dancing loudly around it. My dreams floated me into the room beside her. She was crying. Hideous purple devil's faces pressed mockingly on the grimy windows. The thin miserable auctioneer, skeletal now, stood high above everyone, waving a rope and covered in blood. The cow in Riley's garden died over and over and over again. Its blood pierced the window glass speckling me and Marjorie, who continued to cry long dry sobs, as our mothers marched relentlessly up Neville Street to her front gate.

Tears rolled down my face and I started to shout; louder than the auctioneer, louder than the hysterical crowds in the market, so loud in fact that I woke my sister.

"What's up our Jill?" she muttered, still asleep.

"It's Marjorie," I started to explain but she was already fast asleep with one fat arm linked to my tense bony one.

I avoided Marjorie and the market for weeks until one Monday I was sent to collect a can of milk. Balancing it carefully across the cattle yard, a sudden stampede of hooves and a wild cowboy whooping yell sent me spinning round. Marjorie, wearing her brother's trousers and shirt thundered past astride a beautiful conker-coloured horse. Her yellow hair stuck out like sunshine as she balanced fearlessly bareback controlling the huge animal with the forbidden length of rope. She was right. The cattleman had taught her something special. She looked magnificent.

The sticky sweet milk soaked right through my flowered frock and vest but as I wandered home with pictures of Marjorie in my head, I'd learned two new things. I would never tell my mother anything real again and like Marjorie, if I wanted to do something I would do it, no matter what.

The Large Oval Egg

The large oval egg lay on the nature table, beautiful, perfectly smooth, tempting the child.

She placed a careful finger on its surface and pressed gently. Nothing happened.

She pressed harder until suddenly it split its brittle skin and grabbed her yolk-soaked finger.

"I didn't do it." she cried, with her finger still stuck in the egg.

Waiting for Susan

My cousin had small round feet. Her shoes were always too big. I think they were her sisters. She kicked them off and trotted about without socks. She never spoke but she made interesting noises and I liked her. The rest of my family said she was mad. I loved her cropped frizzy hair and her brown oval eyes. Most of all I liked her small round feet. I envied them and what she did with them.

She would kick high in the air, twizzle and land without falling. She trotted and galloped, rearing, neighing and snorting down her nose. Best of all was when she flung herself at the high garden gate, bouncing her feet to the sky, a tiny, furious bundle of life, smashing into its wooden slats and falling in a dejected heap every time. Her short, white shins were blotched with bruises, but she never gave up.

"Where have you been?" My mother asked.

"Watching Susan", I muttered.

"You've got to stop that. I've told you before. She's funny in the head, it will only encourage her."

"But I like her and she's my cousin", my voice faded.

"I don't care. You're not to go again or I'll tell your dad."

But I did go. Every day of the summer holidays I would sit at the end of her garden, watching.

One warm afternoon, settled under the ripening blackcurrant bushes, drowsy from their dusty scents, I fell asleep, watching for Susan.

Her loud scream woke me, but her silence was more terrifying. She lay in a damp heap at the bottom of the gate. I couldn't wake her.

As they picked her up her shoes slipped off and fell to the ground with a thud.

Nothing fitted Susan.

Making a man

"Shall we make a man?" asked the mother clinking the coal onto the crumpled newspaper.

"Shall we make a really special man, just for us?"

The struck match lit up the child's puzzled face.

"Oh yes. Let's make a man, let's make a man", and the fire crackled through the sticks. Lighting up the dark room. Dancing shadows on the white walls wrapped the cold kneeling figures in a warm haze.

"He can have granddad's jacket," said the mother, " and when he's got a head I'll find him a smart hat."

The child got very excited.

Every day the man grew. The child and her mother stuffed a hessian sack with straw and pulled a waist into it with binding string.

"Put your finger on the knot and hold tight. We don't want his chest to slip down into his bottom."

The child giggled. The arms of the jacket curved forwards into a hug and the child gently held the clumsy gloved hands.

"Hello", she whispered, "you can live with us now."

Old overalls, more straw, wellingtons full of cobwebs and he had a body.

"You can't stand up, so I'll find you a chair."

The headless man sat in the corner of the kitchen. The child loved him. The mother had never heard her child talk so much.

"Listen to what happened at school."

'"I know you can't answer yet."

"I missed you today."

"Are you lonely on your own?"

"I've told my friends all about you, you're famous." And then she whispered,

"Molly said she wished she had a dad like you."

Weeks later, for a surprise, the mother made him a head. She spent all day spooning the yellow mush from an over-ripe pumpkin. Eyes, nose and mouth holes gaped from the bright yellow face. His hat was paper – pink, left over from Christmas. She felt pleased and excited waiting for her child to be dropped off by the school bus.

They met at the gate.

"I've got a big surprise for you."

She placed her hands over the child's eyes as she led her into the kitchen and up to the pumpkin head.

"One, two, three look now."

The child stood perfectly still, fingers clenched. Her eyes brimmed slowly and she started to cry, little wavering dry sobs, as the face grinned hideously into hers. She hid behind her hands, silent tears trickling down her cheeks.

The Allotment

"Go into the allotment and open the shed door."

"Why?"

"It's a surprise. Go when the night is closing in and then she won't be frightened."

"Who won't?"

"Take some chicken feed in your hand and crawl in, close the door behind you quickly."

"What for?"

"Just do it. You won't be disappointed. It's something you've always wanted."

The child did as she was told. Clutching fists of corn she walked to the allotment in the dark. She felt nervous, excited and uncertain. The shed was silent. She pressed her ear against the splintering boards. Something was listening to her. She didn't hear it but she felt it.

Something large leaned against the inside boards and listened back, in the dark.

The corn had grown smaller, it had trickled its Gretel seeds along the path. There was very little left.

She edged towards the door and tried to lift the latch with her small clenched hands. Inside something moved towards her. She smelled its mealy breath and it smelled her. Then she was inside knee-deep in straw in the pitch dark, her arms outstretched, her palms flat, sprinkled with peace offerings.

At first nothing happened. 'It' was perfectly still. She could see its fuzzy outline. It was bigger than her and she knew it was watching, staring through the darkness.

"Are you hungry?" She whispered. "I've brought you some food."

She slowly pushed her hands towards the creature until the tips of her fingers felt its course stiff hair. It shuddered. "Don't be frightened."

With a slight movement it lowered its head and snuffled her fingers, carefully crunching the warm seeds.

"It's a pony", she thought, "I've always wanted a pony." She leaned forward and the movement startled it. It shook its head and dug its hooves in the straw.

She could see more clearly now and what she saw amazed her.
It had one bony horn growing out of its forehead. "It can't be." Very slowly she reached out to touch the horn. It was rigid and warm. The unicorn nuzzled, looking for more seeds.

"It's something you've always wanted." her father had said, and he was right.

Counting to a hundred

The old house was huge and the child loved it. A staircase curled up to the top floor, its banister rail polished. The mother was immediately fearful but the child knew better than to slide down it when she was there.

"Where are you going nan?"

It was difficult to sneak away for a rest.

"I'm going to hide. You must count to a hundred, without any help and then come and find me."

She had discovered this hiding place days ago. Quietly she opened the heavy door and closed it gently behind her. The sun streamed in through the window, dancing the dust flakes over the crumpled sofas, settling them on to the thick carpets and quilted cushions. This was the 'best' room. A piano grinned its silent yellow-toothed smile. Oddly, grandmother smiled back.

Behind the drawn curtains, in the window seat, she relaxed and forgot all about the counting boy. Smears patterned the glass in the old frames; the shapes and shadows of garden birds flew across the curtain backs. She sat dustily still and closed her eyes. The birds were busy and noisy. She knew every song, recognised every conversation and flutter, imagined every argument.

And then the door burst open.

"Nan are you in there?" The child was very wary. This was the posh room, the one you didn't enter unless invited.

"Nan, I know you're in there", his voice swaggered.

"I can see you lying behind the sofa. You're foot's sticking out."

"NAN", he was angry now.

"NAN, you're cheating so I give up."

Moments later she turned her head slowly and watched him outside in the garden angrily kicking fir cones. As she walked down the path he ran towards her.

"Where were you hiding?"

"I'm not telling you."

"Tell me or I won't share my toffees."

"No."

"Tell me, please Nan", he wheedled.

"No."

There was a long pause as he dropped behind her.

"Tell me or I won't pray for you when you die", he thought it was the worst thing he could say.

His grandmother turned her face to him and they both stood perfectly still glaring at each other.

"Then I won't die", she said and smiled. He smiled back and they walked on together.

Go Outside and Play

"Go and play in the snow."

I was six and very thin. "I don't want to. It's cold."

"Of course it's cold. That's why it's good fun. Go and play in the snow."

"I hate cold. I freeze up."

"Don't be silly. Your sister is out there. Look through the window."

"But she's fat. She stays warm."

"This is stupid. Go out and play in the snow." (angry mother's voice)

The next minute my arms were tugged through my sleeves, my wellies pulled up to my knees, and my hat pulled over my eyes. With one sharp push, I shot outside into the icy world of garden.

"Now, go and play in the snow."

I remember the other kids twizzling me. I remember seeing a snowman bigger than I was. I remember being pulled on a sledge for a long time. Then the snow slid over me and my small world vanished.

"Mrs Madden, I think your Jill is dead. She hasn't moved for ages and she's as white as snow."

Then there was a doctor with a flower in his buttonhole; a red flower, and my sister was speaking. "She's only pretending."

Finders Keepers

He walked in wearing a pair of Eric Morecambe glasses. There were no lenses. He wore his own spectacles behind them.

"I found these. They don't work but aren't they great. Can I leave them here with you nan. Mum will chuck them."

The next thing was a blue glass eye. He balanced it behind one of the lenses. I shuddered.

"Wish I could find another one," he said as he stared at the eye mimicking it, scrunching up one of his own eyes.

A tiny damp felt covered badger followed. Two beady eyes shone out from its threadbare face. This was a real prize.

"He cost me nothing and he's perfect. I found him wedged in the grid. It took me ages to get him out"

The light danced inside a glass bottle as he turned it to the sun and a button sized elephant twinkled a silver eye and a rusted tent peg became a very small old man's walking stick.

Two hazelnuts, a fat tight fir cone, one black wooden chess piece and a purple stone followed but his greatest find appeared last week.

"Look nan."

He uncurled his fingers and there, staring at us from the palm of his hand lay a green glass eye.

"I know it's not the same colour," carefully balancing it behind the empty Eric Morecambe frame.

"But it doesn't matter does it?"

Ticket to Sugarloaf

My aunt Cissie was a divorced woman. This was very unusual in the 1940's. When I asked my grandmother why, she said it was because aunt Cissie made her husband rice puddings with water, whereupon he flew into terrible rages and eventually divorced her.

I secretly thought it must be wonderful to be divorced, because, of all my married aunts, she was the happiest. The others were sensible middle-aged ladies with thick ankles. They never threw their heads back and really laughed.

"Ooh, our Cissie!" they'd say with amused disapproval when she smoked and swore and made clever remarks about their husbands.

She was stick-thin with dark hair. 'The plain one' they all called her; "Poor little Cissie!" my mother was always saying. My mother told and retold the story of how, when they were all young, my grandmother had made Cissie a frock out of an old umbrella. I imagined it sticking out in points like a black ballet skirt, Cissie's bony white knees peeping from beneath its sculptured hem, Cissie dancing in the rain and never getting her knickers wet. Then they explained how my grandmother had skinned the umbrella first and carefully hand-sewn it.

So it was with some surprise, when, years later, I was shown a photograph of a young Cissie and discovered her to be a hauntingly delicate young woman with devilish eyes and a quality which I now recognise as 'sex appeal'.

Cissie wasn't sensible; she laughed at the most outrageous things. She read the News of the World and she introduced my sister and me to another world, slightly illicit and secret; a world where men weren't just relatives and where, despite what my grandmother told

85

us, you weren't struck down by God if you drank alcohol or spoke to a Roman Catholic. I didn't know it then, but it was a world in which sex played a vital role and my aunt Cissie was the star.

Bored one day by my grandmother and mother's Sunday dinner ritual, I vanished unnoticed into the 'glory hole', closed the door, switched on the light and began to rummage. I loved rooting in there. It filled me with unbearable excitement, with a wonderful feeling of wrongdoing, especially on a Sunday.

I crawled beneath the hanging coats and pushed my way through the bags and shoes, deep under the darkest wedge of the stairs, and there I found them - two old shoe boxes sealed with crinkled brown sellotape, stored in the only place my grandmother's stiffening body couldn't search.

The boxes held all of Cissie's love letters. As I sat cross-legged on the floor and slid the first one out of its envelope I knew I had opened the door to another world. Here was real knowledge - about life and feelings and passion and pain. As I read that first letter with all its tenderness and hope, all its kisses and gentle loving, the Sunday-dinner world faded and I emerged from the glory hole reborn. I told no one of my visits to the letters.

Aunt Cissie had a gentleman friend, and one Sunday she took my twin sister and me on a bus ride to visit him. "One and two halves to the Sugarloaf!". The bus conductor pressed a metal lever on his ticket machine and I watched, fascinated, as it pushed out three tickets. I jostled my sister to take charge of these, amazed that this machine could produce tickets in halves for twins, and we weren't even identical. I squeezed past my sister to claim a window seat.

Wary of creases, I smoothed my new coat under me and tugged at the edges of my sister's as she concertina'd it beneath her. Janice was already deep in conversation with aunt Cissie, who sat across the aisle clicking open her handbag and scooping handfuls of sweets: shiny, crinkly toffees, twisted in jewelled cellophane - Cissie's treasures.

Wherever she was she had toffees about her. In her pinny pocket were chocolates, not hankies or clothes pegs. In her bed, hidden under her pillow, were Fry's Cream Bars - presents from American soldiers - and in her dressing table drawers, mingled with the beads and clip-on earrings, were packets of chewing gum. Forbidden fruits.

Everything about this day was forbidden. Sworn to secrecy by Cissie, we travelled happily on the top deck of the bus in a cloud of cigarette smoke until we reached our stop at Sugarloaf.

We walked down a country lane warmed by the early spring sunshine. We scrambled up hedges and stole a bird's egg, only to squash it later in the pocket of my best coat. We raced; then dawdled along quiet, overgrown paths, and we laughed, sang, and shouted 'bugger' and 'bloody hell' at the tops of our voices. We made up rude rhymes about people we didn't like; then aunt Cissie stopped at a gate in a hedge.

Cissie snapped open her handbag and took out a little face compact and mirror. Fascinated, I watched as she wound a vivid red lipstick up from its tube and carefully painted her mouth. Next she pinched a flat, bright red powder-puff from its tiny gold case and rubbed roses into her cheeks. Finally, she combed her hair into neat waves, pinching each crest with her fingers.

My sister, head down, kicked about in the long grass looking for four-leafed clovers, but I watched, intrigued by this transformation. We had danced up the lane with our aunt Cissie, but we walked down the path towards an old farmhouse with a film star.

87

A very large lady opened the door. She smelled of dinners and the hen-meal I mixed for our hens. She wiped her hands on her pinny and welcomed us into a dark, warm room where everything was big, faded, and dusty.

The only sign of life came from one corner, where a bell-shaped cage lurched threateningly on its wire spring. Aunt Cissie and Janice had meanwhile disappeared down a corridor, leaving me alone.

A chunk of railway sleeper fed a dying fire in a wide hearth and somewhere a clock ticked loudly.

"Bugger off. Bugger off." screamed the cage, and I moved back to see a large parrot angrily stepping from one scaly foot to the other.

"She wants to come out." The slow, child's voice came from a young woman sitting in the corner of the room. I was startled; I'd thought I was alone.

"Who are you?"

"Iris." This lovely name belonged to a thin, solitary figure huddled in a chair.

"Your auntie's me dad's fancy woman?" It was a question.

"Yes," I replied innocently, proud of how 'fancy' my aunt could look.

"Bloody cheek, bringing you two here," she said. She pulled her skirt up and casually scratched her fire-blotched open legs. I was amazed - not by the fact that she had no knickers on, but by what I saw where knickers should have been: she had hair growing between her legs. I kept staring. Perhaps that was why they sat her in this room on her own.

"Bugger off. Bugger off."

I backed out of the room and hurried along the corridor in search of aunt Cissie and Janice.

I found them swinging on a faded sofa swing. It was suspended from an apple tree, and opposite them, in a bulging striped deckchair, sat a very fat man. He was wearing a grey suit and town shoes. He stood up, linked my auntie's arm in his and led her away, out of sight, around the corner of the house.

I sat in the swing and kicked off hard, lurching the swing too high into the branches, frightened now by the view of the wood's dark centre.

"What are you doing?" shouted my sister, clinging onto my arm.

"Bugger off. Bugger off." I yelled at the top of my voice.

Pebble

It was a huge pebble – smooth and red and placed exactly in the middle of the pavement.

It was a giant among pebbles.

Too smooth to be a rock.

Too elegant to be a stone.

Too big to be in the middle of the pavement.

I went out of my way to walk past it.

Children tried to lift it.

Dogs peed on it.

Old people feared it in the dark.

So I captured it.

Now it sits in my garden, looking ordinary.

It blends in.

It has lost its power.

Learning the Words

I lost my virginity to a boy whose name, I think, was Michael. I remember I was wearing a green dress with covered buttons and green suede shoes with Cuban heels.

At the time, I was teaching in a rough Manchester school, a dark Victorian building surrounded by red brick terraced houses, factories, chimneys, and railway bridges. The railway line ran level with my classroom windows, and the Crewe to Manchester Express regularly took us by surprise, leaving us half-visible and choking on its smoke. It rained a lot.

Punishments were lashed out with a broad leather strap across a child's hands or back by the grey-haired headmistress. The first and only time I saw this happen, I rushed away and was immediately sick in the sink. The ten-year-old child took me back to the classroom, where they all looked after me until I felt better. I never again took a child for punishment, and for the rest of my career in teaching I fought for the abolition of corporal punishment, getting so carried away at one meeting that I finished my speech with "Capital punishment in our schools must end."

Children frightened the headmistress. Wearing thick lisle stockings, laced-up shoes, neat hand-knitted twinset, and knee-length tweed pleated skirt, she only emerged from her office for morning assembly. This was the time when the whole school gathered together for serious thought. Each teacher stood beside her class, anxiously scanning the children for punishable offences. Sniffing, muttering, nudging, giggling, fidgeting, pushing, wanting a wee at the wrong time - all were dealt with by this small neat lady with the thick leather strap. Her pale blue eyes missed nothing as her cold, weak, grey voice preached forgiveness and understanding; love and retribution – particularly retribution. Then we all sang a hymn.

Joy, a solid middle-aged woman, stood to attention next to me. Her entire class of five-year-olds mimicked her every action. If Joy stared at them and straightened her body, they all copied her mannerism. If she pointed her fingers downwards, their little hands strained to imitate hers. When she smiled, they all smiled; when she frowned, they contorted their faces into the same expression.

Fascinated by this mimicry, I once tried to sabotage their behaviour, tempting them to imitate me by standing first on one leg then on the other. I was dutifully ignored while they gazed at Joy. She had trained them well. They loved her, and none of them were ever strapped.

I knew very little about Joy. She made jokes about 'being on the shelf' and referred to herself as 'the spinster of the parish'. It was impossible to imagine her having any life outside of the classroom.

She knew every hymn and sang out loudly, half leaning towards her class, mouthing the words in a ridiculously exaggerated style that they all copied precisely; tiny mirror images.

I sometimes wondered whether they'd grow up into exact 'Joy-clones', boys as well as girls (for there as something asexual about her), but they learned well by mimicking knowledge, spilling out the words long before they ever understood their meaning, and chanting tables like songs.

Intrigued by their learning methods, I once asked Joy if I could observe a maths class and watched a boy, new to the school, rhyme his 2 times table off as if he'd been born knowing it.

"Alan," I praised, "That is so good. Will you sing it on your own for me?"

Full of confidence, he agreed. "Da dee da dee da," he sang, and went on. "Da dee da dee da; da dee da dee da," and, finishing triumphantly, "Dee da."

All the class, led by Joy, applauded. I stared in amazement.

"But, Alan," I questioned naively, "Where are the words?"

I was quickly put in my place.

"I'm new. I only know the tune. I don't know the words yet."

But Joy knew all the words perfectly, so I was taken by surprise one morning when the hymn *To Be A Pilgrim* was commanded by the headmistress, and the terrified mouse of a supply teacher struck up a feeble accompaniment on the piano. Joy turned, winked at me, and sang *To Be A Virgin* instead of 'Pilgrim'. All of her class sang the same words. At first, I couldn't believe it. Watching her lips, waiting for the chorus, she sang it again and again, and the babies' class joined in. I started to blush, then shuffle, then giggle.

"Miss Madden." The headmistress's ice-cold voice cut through the silence as the hymn ended. "Follow me to my office."

I received a punishing lecture. I had set a poor example. I had failed her, and worse, I had failed my pupils with my unseemly behaviour. She abruptly dismissed me.

As I stood outside her door, flushed, angry, and embarrassed, Joy appeared. She stood in front of me, smiling mischievously, two virgins together. And then, she did the most surprising thing; she hugged me, and, holding me at arm's length, said, unexpectedly, "You are twenty-two years of age. It's too late for me. Do something about it." And she was gone, back to her classroom.

As I walked past her room and along the corridor, her class sang out "Da dee da dee da." Yes, I thought, I'm new, but it is time I learned the words.

Which is why I deliberately set off for London in my green dress. My strange experience with Joy had been followed coincidentally by a letter from the young man whose name was almost certainly Michael. We had exchanged intermittent letters after meeting in Jersey one hot, poetic summer. Six weeks of burning sunshine and very little money for food had transformed me into a slender elf-like creature with a head full of dreams. I lived on cornflakes, blackberries, tomatoes, and the local airport's leftover sandwiches. Wearing neither knickers nor shoes, I wandered the dusty evenings soaked in scents and the faintest promise of sin. Serenaded by an invisible orchestra of crickets, my skin glowing and my feet painfully cooled on the gritty road, I was immortal.

Occasionally in my life I have felt beautiful, and on those solitary warm dark walks, unseen, unwashed, and unwanted, I felt truly beautiful. I saw glow-worms for the first time, chasing their fairy lights, trapping them in my hands, only to discover tem to be strangely drab, ugly little insects when imprisoned. So I released them and they released me.

I had met Michael on the last day of that holiday. We exchanged addresses and I never expected to see him again. And then his letter arrived, inviting me to spend a weekend in London, where he was visiting the motor show. I had never been interested in cars, nor was I even interested in London, but Joy's 'Do something about it' still sang in my brain. On the strength of that, I accepted one day and one night in order to act on her advice and ward off a future of thick stockings, laced-up flat shoes, sensible practical behaviour, and conformity.

I stepped across the gap between platform and train, wandered along the corridor and found an empty compartment, clicking myself into it with the heavy sliding door. Reaching up, I pushed my newly bought tapestry-covered bag onto the hammock netting luggage rack and sat neatly in the corner next to the smoky window. As the heavy steam train built up power and snorted slowly out of the station, I turned my collar up, hitched my skirt daringly onto my knees, and pulled a Gauloise cigarette from its distinctive blue crumply packet. I lit up and inhaled deeply.

My head spun and I began to cough. My eyes watered. Gasping for breath, I tried desperately to prise the sliding windows apart. To the rescue came a mother with two children. Late arrivals, they burst into my compartment and spread everywhere.

"Are you all right, lovey?" the woman asked.

Clutching the cigarette in one hand and the open window with the other, I swayed, feeling silly and sick. "I'm fine, thank you," I announced. "It's just that I don't smoke." And I squashed the Gauloise packet into the pocket of my black leather jacket, where it probably remained for at least another two years.

I kept telling myself that I was travelling towards a life-changing weekend; that I would return a completely different person. While other passengers on the station waved and kissed their goodbyes, I looked back at myself and waved goodbye to me as a small child holding her father's hand. I waved goodbye to me as the teenage girl who, racing down the railway station steps, lost her shoe and was unable to keep up with Jack, the real love of her life, when he travelled away on the Manchester train. I watched her standing, crying, on the platform, shoe in hand, an alternative Cinderella, believing the fairy story had ended. And I waved goodbye to me as a student with a case full of books, too proud to let anyone else carry them. I waved goodbye to all of them, and as I did so, my excitement and determination dissolved and my sophistication evaporated. When I stepped off the train in London to a welcome from a happy young man I hardly recognised, I was just a girl in a green frock.

And so it remained. I struggled through a plate of real spaghetti; pale, long, and evasive, and nothing like the bright-orange tinned variety I was used to.

"Aren't you hungry?" he asked.

"No, not really," Gauloise girl replied indifferently, while green frock screamed "Well, I'm starving."

"Would you like a tour of the city?"

"No, not really." Gauloise girl crossed her legs daintily, letting the heel of her green suede shoe slip from her foot.

Green frock, desperately wanting to explore, pleaded, "Oh yes. Let's get on one of those open-top buses and look and point and talk, talk, talk." But nobody heard her. She stood, far away, on Crewe station platform, waving goodbye.

"Would it be possible to go straight to the hotel?" suggested Gauloise girl.

An awkward, embarrassing, uncomfortable afternoon and night followed during which I presume I lost my virginity. I most certainly ended my friendship with the sensitive young man, who, naturally, believed these matters would have been dealt with by then.

I sometimes wonder if he ever thinks of the strange night in the overheated London hotel. Like me, he will be over seventy years of age now. I do hope he had a better time at the motor show.

Fresh Water Well

Dawdling along a rocky beach, searching for shells, I fell behind the other school trip children.

They raced towards the sea shouting and laughing, kicking and pushing, chasing the waves and each other, loud with excitement.

And the silent sun beat down.

As I daydreamed amongst the pebbles and stiff beach grasses I came across a strange silver circle in the sand.

Fresh water, fringed with bright green weed, mirror-still, it held my image crystal clear.

Together we stayed, secret and motionless – a child in a picture, frozen in time, and then I cupped my hands, and, reaching into the ice-cold water, I scooped up my reflection and drank.

Startled, a large green mottled frog swam silently across the ruffled surface of my face, and disappeared.

I wanted to stay there forever, and, in a way, I have.

Jill

I've just discovered, too late,
that Jill means
'youthful' and 'sweetheart'

What a pity that when I fitted those descriptions
the only other Jills I knew were ferrets
with bristly nicotine-stained fur and pink eyes
I put them down holes to catch rabbits
and one bit me so hard that I nearly lost the end of my finger

Now I realise that I should have been skipping through those fields,
a youthful sweetheart to some pretty boy who asked me out when I
was fourteen

I can no longer skip
and I am no longer youthful

But I can skin a rabbit!

Evelyn

New Zealand February 1934

Evelyn knew no one when she arrived in New Zealand for the second time. It had been ten years since she last worked there and felt proud of her independence. She felt safe within it. She had worked hard and saved money. It was the only praise she ever received from her mother. "Thank God you're good with money our Evelyn. You'll never need to depend on a man."

Her mother had run a corner shop and was a good businesswoman. She always carried a leather pouch full of coins strapped around her waist. She once showed Evelyn some gold coins. Evelyn wondered if her mother slept with the pouch full of money.

Evelyn placed her money in the Wellington Savings Bank and had it forwarded to the Girls Friendly Society at Napier. She fiercely guarded her passbook and had it sent out to Walpana where she hoped to find work.

The Evening Post Napier, April 12th 1935

Edward Mervyn Murray, a bank clerk at Hastings identified three cheques, which he cashed for a woman on February 5th. They totalled £8.15.9d. They were drawn in favour of Evelyn Madden.

Evelyn was a good hard worker and soon after she landed in New Zealand she found a job as a domestic servant at Oreka sheep station. It was owned by Mr Lowry who had once played tennis for Cambridge University and she liked the English connection. She enjoyed the routine. The work gave her time to think. She missed her family, especially her father. Each night she wrote long letters telling them about the countryside, its bleakness and its space. It was so different from Cheshire with its small-hedged fields, tall oak trees and ponds. Back home nearly every field had a pond where she would go with her brothers and catch newts with their plain and orange bellies, crested newts which lay in the mud like sleeping dragons and hundreds of water beetles pinging to the surface to collect life giving bubbles of air.

The children would breed secret maggots on rotten meat, tie them with cotton and lower them into the water. Almost immediately a newt would swallow the bait and appear wet and wriggling on the end of the cotton. Pulling it off gently meant she could use the same maggot for her next catch, while the captured newt waddled off into the long grass, away from the sun. She was intrigued that these creatures could breathe air and then water. It was magical.

Daily Telegraph, local Napier newspaper

Body in creek; originally thought to be Maori or half-caste.

It was unwise to wander too far away from the sheep station alone. Evelyn had made one friend. He was part of the farm team who, when sober was a cheerful man. He accompanied her on several long walks and understood the landscape with its limestone crops and dangerous creeks. Charles talked to Evelyn on these walks.

"I was off by the time I was twelve. Our old man was either mad or drunk."

"But didn't you miss your family?" Evelyn thought about her dad.

"I bloody didn't. Felt safer without them. Never went back."

Evelyn slowly began to understand his moods. One day, just outside the farmstead they found a tree tied to a support stake it had long ago outgrown. The twine was now cutting deep into its bark and Charles spent ages with his knife freeing it.

"There you are mate, you can breathe now." He smiled.

Evelyn slipped her hand into his as they walked on. He described strange fish with rasping mouths, attached to rocks or woody logs, hidden in streams, shy and nocturnal, frightened of hunting birds that couldn't fly. Sometimes she wondered if he was making it up. Birds that didn't fly and frogs that didn't croak. She would laugh about this.

They would lie in the tufted dusty grass and look up at the sky. The bellbirds would tell their songs in the sticky heat. "Karimako is their Maori name." He said.

"Tell me the name of the strange fish again?" She'd ask.

"Kanakana, the Maoris used to eat them but I never did."

"Kanakana, Kanakana." She'd repeat. "I like the sound of that."

She talked to him about Cheshire and its wildlife. She told him all about her family and friends. He was a good listener, but a heavy drinker. After a while he seemed to stop listening altogether and would concentrate on the dry gin, which he carried in his pocket. Occasionally she'd see him drink methylated spirit mixed with water from the creek and then smash the empty bottle against a rock. It irritated him that she would never join him in a drink. Nearly always they had fallen out by the time they'd get back to the sheep station.

She enjoyed the company though and when he announced he was leaving his job she was surprised how sorry she felt.

"Why don't you come with me?" he'd asked

Evelyn told no one about her money. She always carried some, hidden away in her petticoats. She knew that she could survive. She had excellent references from Mr Lowry who was well respected. She was not a risk taker.

Her two locked suitcases held all her belongings. Her cabin trunk remained at the storage at Hastings railway station. She carried all her keys in a safe bundle and she enjoyed her time preparing for the journey.

Appearance was important to Evelyn and she paid great attention to detail. She chose good quality, hardwearing materials and blended colours well. Her shoes were comfortable, fashionable and shiny and her jewellery was plain but unusual. She set off to meet Charles Price in her smartest outfit.

Daily Telegraph, Napier, Saturday 16th February 1935

Victim identified as Miss Madden, died of severe injuries to the head. Violent murder is responsible for her death. The body is estimated to have been three weeks in the waterhole at the creek.

She was hoping that he'd stay sober but she knew that she'd got 'safety money' and the adventure of it excited her. She was normally careful and self-disciplined but their decisions to travel were enticing. She would make this move and write her letters later. She knew her family and friends would be interested by this change of course and she decided she might even tell them about Charles.

She'd directed money to be collected at Napier, her passbook had been sent to Walpawa and she'd filled in an application form to withdraw the sum of £30. She also arranged for money to arrive at the Girls Friendly Society lodge where she intended to stay.

Evening Post, Napier

A housemaid employed by the Girls Friendly Society at Napier said that a woman accompanied by a man, called at the lodge on February 5th, seeking lodgings. The money had not arrived. The woman who said her name was Madden, decided not to stay at the lodge and departed with the man, who waited outside the gate. The money order telegram arrived at the lodge for Miss Madden that afternoon and has remained unclaimed.

Evelyn was disappointed that her money had not arrived in advance. She expected her plans to unfold like maps and lead her along in her chosen direction. As she walked back to Charles, who had waited at the gate, she made a decision. He had been good company buoyed up by the £3 she had given him. He hadn't spent it all on drink either. He had bought them both food and he had started to talk about their life together. It was a comfortable feeling to be cared for. She left the Girls Friendly Society and travelled on with him to Hastings, where they booked into the Hastings Hotel together.

Charles Price was a man used to getting his own way. He was wary of staying in any one place for too long, it made him feel trapped and threatened. He needed to drink. His biggest fear was sobriety. He liked Evelyn Madden. It was unusual to find a woman who was not afraid of being alone, even more unusual to find one who was financially independent. He had been glad to leave his wife.

When he had walked out of Lowry's place the cook, Audrey Jamieson, laughingly asked him, "Are you and Evelyn going off on honeymoon together?"

"No I'm sick of her and I'm sick of this job." He'd replied. " I need a rest."

But he wasn't sick of her.

He used the rest of the money to buy drink, keeping enough by to pay for a taxi to Taheke. He'd remembered on one of their walks Evelyn had mentioned a Mrs Hollis who lived in Taheke district. She had made friends with this woman and might even find work there. She had wanted to visit her but he'd thought it was a waste of time.

As Evelyn got ready he continued to drink. He felt better. The taxi was due at 2pm and they'd soon be on the move.

Daily Telegraph, Napier, Saturday 16th February, 1935

This mystery may develop into one of the most revolting murders in criminal history, in New Zealand.

Description of victim

5ft 4", well built, well nourished, brown coloured hair, wearing a cotton print dress with a v yoke and brown coloured collar fastened with a bow at the front. The material is cotton with a design of oval-shaped terracotta red and chocolate brown dots on a white background. It has 3" sleeves piped to match the collar. She was wearing two petticoats, the outer one made of linen with lace on the bottom hem but a plain top hem. The inner one was finer with lace top and bottom and silk shoulder straps. The victim also wore a finely woven singlet apparently of silk and wool brown stockings and brown elastic garters.

Evelyn dressed carefully. She had liked Mrs Hollis and wondered if she'd remember how they had met when on holiday, years ago at Masterton. They had become friendly and Mrs Hollis had told Evelyn that she had come from the old country. She had given Evelyn a string of beads as a goodbye present and Evelyn had never forgotten her.

Daily Telegraph, Napier

The victim's shoes were size 4, black kid with a single strap over the instep and high heels. They bore rubber stick-on soles with the name Joy-Ped and showed little signs of wear. A string of imitation pearl beads large in front to small at the back and spaced with clear glass beads was found around her neck. The fastening was a white metal spring clasp.

As Evelyn walked down the stairs of the Hasting Hotel and into the bar she knew immediately that Charles was drunk. A wave of anger bubbled up inside her but she didn't let it show. It had been her decision to make the journey and she'd see it through to the end. The taxi was late. The driver explained that he didn't know the area and that Price would have to direct him. Evelyn dreaded the journey to Taheke sheep station. She suffered badly from carsickness and felt it as soon as she climbed into the back seat. Charles smoked heavily and continued to drink from a whiskey flask, talking to Norman Guild, the driver, in a loud voice.

She felt dizzy and was relieved to hear Charles organising a stop.

"You're white as a sheet, get some fresh air." She remembered the driver saying. It was then that Charles made a change of plan. He decided that the journey was too far by car and he was going to take Evelyn to Hollis' place by a short cut. He instructed the driver to wait for him as it might take an hour or two.

Evelyn was relieved, as she'd been dreading the continuing car journey. She reached into the back seat for her coat, folded it carefully and carried it over her arm.

They walked down a track, over a hill and lost sight of the waiting taxi. It was good to breathe the fresh air.

The taxi driver curled up on the front seat and had a doze, it was warm and silent. An hour and twenty minutes later Price returned alone along the road, saying he had left the girl at Hollis' place. His feet were wet. He said he'd slipped while stepping over a creek.

Before she'd left, he said Miss Madden had given him £30. He paid the driver £2 from a roll of money which included one or two five pound notes, and told him they would be meeting Miss Madden in the morning at Hastings railway station.

The Evening Post, 11th April 1935

Boy's Discovery

A sixteen-year-old boy, Herbert Bert Mark, a farmhand of Argyll East, described the discovery of the body in Taheke creek. Last January, he said he set an eel trap in the creek. On the evening of February 14th he visited the trap. After walking up the creek some distance and crossing the creek on a log he discovered the body of a woman lying under a willow tree in a hole. The body was about four foot from the bank floating face upwards. He ran to tell his father and the police were communicated with.

When Charles Price was sentenced in court there was a deathly silence. The jury returned after sixty-nine minutes and he was asked if he had anything to say why sentence of death should not be passed on him. He replied, "No."

The dread sentence itself he received with outward calmness. As Mr Justice Blair donned the black cap and slowly pronounced the words which condemned him to die, the only sign of nervousness the prisoner gave was the drumming of his fingers on the dock rail.

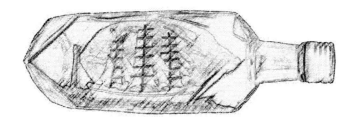